Lift Up Your Eyes on High

UNDERSTANDING THE STARS

James Nickel

Christian Liberty Press

Originally titled *The Heavens Declare: Understanding the Stars*
Originally published by Light Educational Ministries in 1998

Light Educational Ministries
P.O. Box 966
Dickson, ACT 2602, Australia

This edition is republished with permission and by special arrangement of the original publisher.

Published by

Christian Liberty Press

502 West Euclid Avenue
Arlington Heights, IL 60004
www.christianlibertypress.com

Written by James Nickel, B.A., B.Th., M.A.
Layout and editing by Edward J. Shewan
Copyediting by Diane C. Olson

ISBN 978-1-930367-37-1
        1-930367-37-6

Credits

> ➤ Galaxy photographs courtesy of the National Aeronautics and Space Administration (NASA).
> ➤ Zodiac graphics courtesy of Jono Willis, State of the Art Illustrations, Canberra, ACT, Australia.

TABLE OF CONTENTS

TABLE OF FIGURES

FORWARD

Stars have a divine purpose. They reveal the power and wonder of God and are signs which "declare the glory of God" (Psalm 19:1–4; Romans 10:17–18). Indeed, they have a "speech" which they pour forth to all men.

From the Scriptures we can see that God has used the stars in many ways: to give light (along with the Sun and Moon) upon Earth, to confirm His promises to Abraham, to prophecy through a dream the calling of Joseph, to direct magi to the birthplace of the Messiah, and to symbolize earthly and heavenly rulers in terms of their rise and fall.

For our dominion living on Earth, the stars help in the planning of seasonal activities, to find south and north, and to measure time and astronomical distances.

Surely, for the Christian, the stars are more than just balls of superheated gas thrown out into the void by some primeval explosion. How did they originate? What distances and magnitudes typify them? What about astrology? Do stars have a divine purpose?

In helping us to begin to answer these questions, James Nickel has shown that the stars do have significance beyond being physical matter. They bear witness of God's plan of redemption, for He named the stars and even calls groups of them by constellational names (see Psalm 147:4 and Amos 5:8). This is not "astrology" as practiced in the modern sense, but points to God's control over and plan for this part of His creation. There are no "accidental" arrangements in the heavens: God works "all things according to the counsel of His will" (Ephesians 1:11) and "all things" includes the stars!

In *Lift up Your Eyes on High: Understanding the Stars* the author has admirably expanded our vision concerning these heavenly bodies. In the pages of this book the reader will find many facts, parallelisms, interpretations, and questions that should help him or her to "consider the heavens." For the teacher, this book should be a great source of material to inspire students, whether as a key reference, comprehensive text, or even as a workbook where students could fill in matching star names and meanings on diagrams. I have used this book in its first edition form, along with some of the references from the bibliography, in an astronomy course. This course has been the highlight of a secondary science program. Some students have even wanted to do it twice—surely a sign of a successful study!

For those of us in the Southern Hemisphere, the stars bear special witness to the redemptive love of God. The constellation, The Southern Cross, appears on several flags and is a clear redemptive image. Could it be one of the "constellations of the south" mentioned in Job 9:9? Similarly, the image of a mighty man (Ophiuchus) struggling with a serpent (Serpens) while a scorpion (Scorpio) looms threateningly below reminds us of Genesis 3:15 and the suffering Savior-seed from Eve. *Lift Up Your Eyes on High* offers these glimpses and more insights into the wonder and mystery of the night sky.

The reader will find much to ponder in *Lift Up Your Eyes on High*. May it encourage you to pursue further study of the heavens and reclaim the starry realm for Christian appreciation and education.

> Lift your eyes on high, and see Who has created these things, Who brings out their host by number; He calls them all by name, by the greatness of His might and the strength of His power; not one is missing (Isaiah 40:26).

Peter Cain
Light Educational Ministries
Canberra, Australia

PREFACE

Young people are naturally fascinated with and curious about the stars. With more information available through new technology and the continuous expectation that "the stars will guide," secondary students are surrounded with messages about the stars. On the whole, however, they are ill informed and "cheated" in their study of the stars. Study conducted in schools tends to reflect a dichotomous view and generally do not provide the opportunity for holistic studies where one can learn not only scientific "facts," but also of the amazing message the stars declare.

This book provides parents and teachers with an excellent basis to turn the unknown into a tool that both inspires and strengthens one's faith and can raise questions about the real nature of the universe and the amazing God of whom it speaks.

The development stage we call adolescence is characterized by a desire to find answers to the basic philosophical questions: Who am I? Why am I here? What is the reason for living? Is there life after death? Many turn to the Zodiac pages in the newspapers or magazines for input into their life—but do not find the truth there. How much better if they knew of the amazing Gospel truth the stars declare. In this most recent book from James Nickel, the reader will find strengthening of their faith and equipping in their ability to speak back into the society and culture around them.

In its first edition form, this book was an answer to prayer for me in the following situation. On a school excursion with secondary students from a Christian school, I was amazed to watch as these young people, almost without exception, turned first to the Zodiac pages of the free on-board magazine. I realized that they were confused and without knowledge. Knowing that such people are open to deception, we began a series of lessons based on the first edition to show them the richness and life which God has provided, the way in which the heavens indeed declare His love, purpose, and design. Instead of wondering what the answers to the key questions of life are, they could be sure. The culminating activity for this study was the development of their own tract to declare the message of the stars to young people like themselves.

I recommend this book to you if you are a parent or teacher who is committed to equipping young people to be effective in the world in which they live. This book provides you with a resource to equip them so that the next time they are asked about their star sign, they can confidently reply concerning the true message contained within the stars that speak. We are directed by Paul the Apostle in Philippians 2:14–16 (NIV) to "shine like stars in the universe … as you hold out the word of life."

How can we do this if we do not *understand the stars*?

Beverly Norsworthy
MASTERS Institute
Auckland, New Zealand

ABOUT THE AUTHOR

James Nickel holds B.A. (Mathematics), B.Th. (Theology and Missions), and M.A. (Education) degrees. He has been involved in the Christian school movement since 1978 serving as a teacher, home school parent, researcher, lecturer, and writer. He is the author of *Mathematics: Is God Silent?* (Ross House Books, 1990) and *The Heavens Declare: Understanding the Stars* (Light Educational Ministries, 1998). He is currently working on two new books, *Mathematics: Building on Foundations* (which explores the nature, structure, and purpose of mathematics starting from explicit biblical presuppositions) and *Mathematics: The Language of Science*.

He and his wife Lila make their home in Shreveport, Louisiana; they have three grown children—Daniel, Joy, and Margaret. He is currently the Dean of the School of Mathematics of Christian Heritage Academy International, a proposed biblical Christian distance learning school developed in association with Patria Ministries of Washington state and, while performing these duties, he is also writing some database applications as a consultant using the small business software package Alpha Five.

He endeavors to work for the cause of biblical Christian reformation heeding the injunction that "true reformation begins with biblical scholarship read and applied."

Chapter One

Introduction

Have you ever taken the time and effort to find a place away from city lights on a clear, moonless night and look up? If you have, then you know the meaning of the "inspiring enchantment of awe." What you are gazing at is the grandest view that we can have of the physical universe in which we live. The author can remember taking his then three-year old daughter out for her first look at the stars. They first positioned a sleeping bag on the cool ground. Lying supinely with her on his chest, they fixed their eyes on high. As her eyes became dark adapted,[1] she began to spontaneously cry, "Oh … Ah … Look!"

One of the goals of this book is to motivate the reader to "lift your eyes on high" and behold the intricate wonders revealed by gazing at the night sky. It is also the goal of the author to encourage the reader to view these wonders from a biblical perspective. These wonders came into being, not as the result of eons of chance processes, but by the creative decree of the God of the Bible.

Let us commence our voyage of wonder by first asking and answering a few important questions.

What is a star?

By scientific definition, a star is a ball of fire like our Sun, a gigantic atomic furnace. It is a large globe of intensely heated gas, shining by its own light. At its surface, a star can reach temperatures of thousands of degrees; in its interior, its temperatures can reach millions of degrees. When it is this hot, a nuclear reaction[2] occurs, which explains the energy source of a star.

The size of an average star is extremely large. An average sized star can hold more than a million Earths. Some are so big that thirty thousand million of our Suns could fit into them! (We can write this number in a shorter version by using scientific notation. Using this notation, it becomes 3×10^{10}).

How many stars?

On a clear, bright night, you could, with the naked eye, count between three to five thousand stars in about two hours. Scientists call stars seen with the naked eye lucid stars. Lucid stars make up a very small proportion of the total number of stars in the universe.

---

1. What happens when the human eye, under little or no illumination, becomes increasingly sensitive to light from distant objects.
2. Conversion of hydrogen into helium.

Modern science has given us powerful tools with which we can explore the heights of the heavens. Astronomers tell us that within the range of the largest telescope there are 10^{11} (one followed by eleven zeros) galaxies[3] with each galaxy containing about 10^{11} stars. Using the arithmetic of powers, we multiply 10^{11} by 10^{11} and discover that there are 10^{22} stars within telescopic range.

But we are not finished yet. Albert Einstein estimated that the number of stars in total space is 10,000 (10^4) times larger than the number of stars within telescopic range ($10^{22} \times 10^4 = 10^{26}$). How large is the number 10^{26}? Counting one number every second, it would take three thousand trillion centuries to do it! With the recent invention of the radio telescope, stars that give no visible light can be "heard." In our own galaxy, one of the 10^{11} observable galaxies, there are 10^{11} such radio stars! The human mind cannot even begin to fathom the exact magnitude of the number of stars in the heavens.

How far away are they?

The closest star to Earth is Alpha Centauri[4] (below our southern horizon[5]). It is one pointer to the constellation called the Southern Cross or Crux. It is about 2.54×10^{13} miles away.

Astronomers use special mathematical techniques (see Appendix Seven and its discussion of parallax) to measure these stellar distances. These distances are so great that standard distance units like miles soon become useless. To rectify this, astronomers have created a new unit of measure, called the light-year. A light-year is the distance that light travels in one year.

Light travels at an amazing 186,000 miles per second. How fast is this? If we had a space vehicle that could travel at this speed, we could orbit Earth seven times in one second! We could reach the Moon in two seconds, the Sun in eight minutes, and the planets in a couple of hours.

In one year, light travels about 5.87×10^{12} miles (186,000 miles/sec. times 31,556,926 sec./year). Therefore, Alpha Centauri is 4.3 light-years from Earth (2.54×10^{13} divided by 5.87×10^{12}). How far away is this? Let us represent Earth by a marble. The Sun, the size of a medicine ball,[6] would sit about 300 yards away. Alpha Centauri would be about 50,000 miles away! By way of another model, let us represent Earth by a mote—a speck of dirt just barely visible to the naked eye. The Sun, one inch in diameter, would be three yards away, and Alpha Centauri would be 400 miles away.

The astronomical unit (AU) is another common unit of measure. It is the distance between Earth and the Sun (approximately 93,000,000 miles). One light-year would be equal to 63,245 AU; therefore, the distance of Alpha Centauri from Earth is 271,953.5 AU.

One way to help us comprehend the immensity of the visible universe is to shrink it down. For example, the diameter of the Milky Way galaxy is about 100,000 light-years. From Earth, we can see stars in all directions at a maximum of 1.4×10^{10} light-years away (radius from Earth). Looking from a different viewpoint, let's say our galaxy is four inches in diameter. The visible universe would extend from Earth in a nine-mile radius (eighteen-mile diameter). You would find another galaxy like ours every twenty-five to thirty-five inches uniformly distributed throughout that eighteen-mile diameter!

3.　A galaxy is a gigantic gathering of stars, gas, and dust, all bound together by gravity.
4.　Alpha Centauri has a companion star, Proxima Centauri, that is thought to be slightly nearer to us than Alpha.
5.　The horizon is the boundary between the sky and the Earth. It is the place where the sky seems to meet the surface of the Earth.
6.　A solid weighted ball tossed for exercise and is usually thirteen inches in diameter; originally a leather-ball, but is now made of plastic.

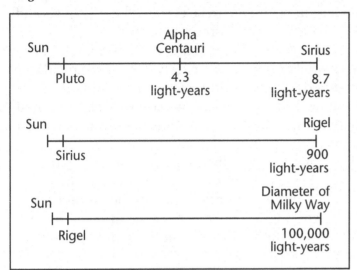

Figure 1–1: The Distant Stars

Astronomers often speak of distances such as 100,000 light-years and more. The Andromeda galaxy (catalogued as M31[7]) is estimated to be about 2.2 million light-years away. For those who believe the biblical doctrine of a recent creation, these great distances expose an apparent contradiction. This doctrine says that the universe is the product of an act of creation only 6,000 to 10,000 years ago.[8] If this is so, many people ask, "How is it that we can see objects millions of light-years away? Surely such light would take millions of years to reach us." Several answers can help a biblical Christian to respond to such questions.

As preparatory background, we must realize that people are thinking in evolutionary terms when they ask this question. The questioner is presupposing an evolutionary view of the stars.[9] At a certain point in the past, because of one evolutionary process or another, a specific star acquired a sufficient level of energy to start emitting light rays. These rays then began to travel across billions of miles of space until they eventually reached us. Note that scientists have never seen a star evolve and their ideas about star evolution are entirely speculative.

A first possible answer comes from a study of the fourth day of creation. Genesis 1:17 says, "And God set them (Sun, Moon, and stars) in the firmament of the heaven to give light upon the earth." The implication is that light from the stars reached Earth immediately. God created the stars with light from them already reaching Earth. Look at a star that tonight is at a distance of 100,000 light-years. God created this star at an instant of time only 6,000 to 10,000 years ago. God supplied the light from all those other supposed years in His instant act of creation.[10]

Physicist D. Russell Humphreys has developed an interesting thesis that explains how this could have happened. His conclusions are based upon Albert Einstein's general theory of relativity that posits an expanding cosmos where clocks (and all physical processes) tick at different rates in different parts of the universe. These different rates can be verified experimentally. The force that causes this phenomenon is called *gravitational time dilation*.[11] According to Humphreys, during the fourth day of creation, billions of Earth years elapsed in the distant sky, allowing light from galaxies to reach Earth within one ordinary day of Earth's time.[12]

The Australian astronomer Barry Setterfield has proposed a second possible answer to this question.[13] His studies have shown a decreasing trend over the past 300 years in the computed speed of light. For example, in 1675 Olaus Roemer computed the speed of light to be 186,806 miles/sec., ±

7. According to the French astronomer Charles Messier's (1730–1817) late eighteenth century compilation of galaxies.
8. We know these approximations through the study of Bible chronology. See Philip Mauro, *The Wonders of Bible Chronology* (Swengel, PA: Reiner Publications, n.d.).
9. See Chapter Two, the section entitled "Facts and Faith" for more detail.
10. See Henry Morris, *The Genesis Record* (Grand Rapids: Baker Book House, 1976), pp. 65–68.
11. W. Rindler, *Essential Relativity*, rev. 2nd ed. (New York: Springer-Verlag, 1977), p. 21.
12. D. Russell Humphreys, *Starlight and Time: Solving the Puzzle of Distant Starlight in a Young Universe* (Colorado Springs, CO: Master Books, 1994).
13. For more information on his studies write to Creation Science Foundation Ltd., P. O. Box 6302, Acacia Ridge D.C. Qld., 4110, Australia, Creation Science Foundation (N.Z.), Fowey Lodge, 215 Bleakhouse Road, Howick, Auckland, New Zealand, or Master Books, P.O. Box 26060, Colorado Springs, CO 80936.

125. In 1976, scientists have computed the speed of light to be 185,871.32 miles/sec. His resulting thesis: The speed of light is not constant; i.e., the speed of light was significantly higher in the past.

If Setterfield's statistics and mathematical model can be proven to be correct,[14] then light could have reached Earth from the farthest visible object in only a very short time—only 6,000 years ago. His statistical analysis shows that, about 4000 B.C., the speed of light began decreasing. If c (speed of light) was greater in the past, radioactive decay would occur more rapidly. Scientists calculate enormous age ranges by applying radiometric methods on rocks. Underlying these methods is the assumption that c is constant. These radiometric dates and their exceptions can now be explained using Setterfield's slowing of light theory; i.e. they become shortened to some 6,000 years, instead of being evidence for great age.

A third possible answer considers the space idea proposed by Albert Einstein's special relativity theory. Einstein's theory says that light does *not* travel in a straight line (as stipulated in Euclidean geometry), but along curved surfaces. The nineteenth century German mathematician Bernhard Riemann formulated this non-Euclidean idea. In essence, you can leave the stars at their "astronomical" locations in Euclidean space. Yet the light from these stars can get to us in very small periods of time—at the most 15.71 years.[15]

Where did God place the stars?

God set them [Sun, Moon, and stars] in the firmament of the heavens... (Genesis 1:17).

What does the Bible mean by the phrase, "firmament of the heavens?" To understand this phrase, we must return to the first two verses of Genesis 1.

In the beginning God created the heavens and the earth. And the earth was without form, and void; and darkness was on the face of the deep. And the Spirit of God was hovering over the face of the waters (Genesis 1:1–2).

Figure 1–2: The Deep

The Heavens

The Deep

A straightforward reading of the text would indicate that Earth was originally a shapeless and lifeless region located within what might have been a sphere of waters called "the deep." Over the surface (or face) of the deep was darkness. The heavens were above the deep. The Spirit of God is pictured as hovering over the surface of the deep. In Genesis 1:3–5, God speaks light into existence. This light source is more than likely the outshining, radiant glory of God and could be linked to the hovering Spirit of God. This same light appears again in the shekinah radiance (glory cloud) localized in the holy of holies of the tabernacle/temple complex and in the New Jerusalem of the new heavens and earth, i.e., the Church (see Revelation 21:23; 22:5; Hebrews 12:22–24). Using this luminary source, God divided the light from the darkness and the creation experienced its first day—evening and morning. This means that the deep was rotating. A reference point on the surface of the deep would have rotated full circle—from the dark side of the deep to the light side of the deep—marking off one complete day.[16]

---

14. Setterfield's statistics and modeling have been challenged. See E. F. Caffin, "A Determination of the Speed of Light in the Seventeenth Century," *Creation Research Society Quarterly* 29:3 (1992): 115–120.

15. See Harold S. Slusher, *Age of the Cosmos* (San Diego: Institute for Creation Research, 1980), pp. 33–37. Slusher's work is based upon a paper published by Parry Moon and Domina Spencer in the August, 1953 issue of the *Journal of the Optical Society of America*.

16. The Word of God states that the creation took place in six twenty-four hour days. If not, then Exodus 20:9–11, part of the Ten Commandments, is deceiving us. God does *not* deceive us with His word.

The events of day two contribute to an engaging analysis:

> Then God said, "Let there be a firmament in the midst of the waters, and let it divide the waters from the waters." Thus God made the firmament, and divided the waters which *were* under the firmament from the waters which *were* above the firmament; and it was so. And God called the firmament Heaven.... (Genesis 1:6–8).

On day two, God made a firmament or expanse.[17] In the middle of the waters of the deep, God let this firm material exist. This firmament separated the waters—there are now waters below and above the firmament. How did God do this? There are a significant number of passages in Scripture indicating that God "stretched or spread out" the heavens. Psalm 104, a psalm of creation, states in verse two that God stretched out the heaven like a tent curtain.[18] It seems that God separated the waters by first placing the firmament in the middle and then stretched the firmament out. God called this firmament heaven.

The created universe now has two sets of waters. One is below the firmament and the other above the firmament. On day three, God gathered the waters below the firmament into one place, let dry land appear, and called the dry land Earth (Genesis 1:9–10). The water above the firmament could possibly be a spherical water boundary encircling the firmament, what we know now as interstellar space.

Above this boundary, there exists the highest heaven, or the heaven of heavens (I Kings 8:27). The Apostle Paul spoke of the third heaven, called Paradise (II Corinthians 12:2). There are, therefore, three heavens:

1. The firmament, known as interstellar space, created on day two. As we look upward toward the first heaven, we gaze through Earth's atmosphere, signified in Scripture

Figure 1–3: The Structure of the Heavens

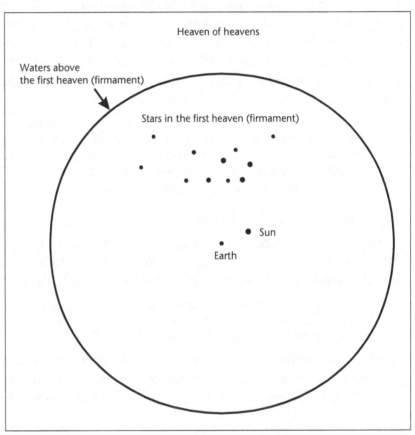

Heaven of heavens

Waters above
the first heaven (firmament)

Stars in the first heaven (firmament)

Sun

Earth

as "the face of the firmament" (Genesis 1:20). On day four, God created lights (Sun, Moon, and the innumerable stars of all 10^{11} galaxies) and placed them in this firmament (Genesis 1:17). This firmament is a public display of "His handiwork" (Psalm 19:1).

---

17. The Hebrew, *raqia*, means "extended surface." It comes from the verb, *raqa*, which means "to stamp, spread out, or expand." The Septuagint's translation (Hebrew to Greek) for this word is *stereoma*. It means "what is made firm."

18. See also Job 9:8; 26:7; 37:18, Isaiah 40:22; 42:5; 44:24; 45:12; 48:13; 51:13, Jeremiah 10:12; 51:15, and Zechariah 12:1. The Hebrew, *natah*, means to "extend, stretch out, or spread out." The Hebrew words in these verses translated as "spread out" come from the verbs *matach*, *taphach*, or *raqa*. The last verb, from Job 37:18, is linked to the noun "expanse" (*raqia*) in Genesis 1. (See footnote 17.) Note the use of simile (a figure of speech in which two essentially unlike things are compared using the words "like" or "as") in the phrase, "God stretched out the heavens *like* a tent curtain." That God stretched the heavens in some manner is established. This stretching is compared to what happens when you stretch a tent curtain.

2. Above the first heaven, beyond the reach of the most distant galaxy, is a spherical wall of water. This wall separates the first heaven from the second heaven, called in Scripture the heaven of heavens. God created the second heaven on day one. We know that even this heaven cannot contain God (I Kings 8:27); that is, it is finite in extent.

3. We know that the third heaven is Paradise. This is where God dwells and His throne is established (Isaiah 66:1; Psalm 11:4). All the angels surround His throne is majestic and glorious praise and worship. Where is this heaven? In one sense, it exists in another dimension, a dimension of spirit, infinitely near to us, yet also infinitely far away.[19] Does it also physically exist somewhere beyond the "waters above the heavens"? Job 22:12 states, "Is not God in the height of heaven? And see the highest stars, how lofty they are!" It appears from Scripture that God manifests His glory[20] *beyond* the stars. His glory is set above the heavens (see Psalm 8:1; 113:4–6). He has to "humble Himself" in order to see the things that are in heaven and on Earth! The Bible does not reveal the specific locality of His glorious dwelling place above the stars, but some hints are given (see Chapter Two, under the discussion of Polaris).

We can derive two important conclusions from this discussion. First, matter in the universe is bounded. It has an edge and center. Earth is most likely located near the center of the material universe and the waters above the firmament form the boundary of the material universe. In contrast, most evolutionary scientists arbitrarily posit that the universe is unbounded. It has no edge or center. Earth has no special place in the cosmos. Note the comments by British theoretical physicist Stephen Hawking (1942–) and George Ellis:

> However we are not able to make cosmological models without some admixture of ideology. In the earliest cosmologies, man placed himself in a commanding position at the centre of the universe. Since the time of Copernicus we have been steadily demoted to a medium sized planet going round a medium sized star on the outer edge of a fairly average galaxy, which is itself simply one of a local group of galaxies. Indeed we are now so democratic that we would not claim our position in space is specially distinguished in any way. We shall ... call this assumption the *Copernican principle*.[21]

Note the phrase, *admixture of ideology*. The assumption of the *Copernican principle* is not based upon observational fact, but upon a pre-commitment to an ideology (for more detail, see the section in Chapter Two subtitled "Facts and Faith"). Note the comments of astrophysicist Richard Gott:

> In astronomy, the Copernican principle works because, of all the places for intelligent observers to be, there are by definition only a few special places and many non-special places, so you are likely to be in a non-special place.[22]

These eminent astrophysicists have basically defined the biblical God out of the picture. Using the words of Harvard Genetics professor Richard Lewontin, they "cannot allow a Divine Foot in the door."[23] To them, we are on this planet as the result of random and violent processes only—not

---

19. In Psalm 22:3, we see that God "sets up His throne" upon the praises of His people. God's throne is as close to us as the praises upon our lips. In Isaiah 6, the prophet sees God sitting on His throne, lofty and exalted, dwelling in unapproachable light (I Timothy 6:16). God's holiness creates an infinite chasm of separation between sinful man and Himself. The proposition that a holy God can dwell in the praises of sinful man is simply amazing. John Newton, the songwriter of old, said it better than anyone could, "Amazing grace." The blood of Jesus Christ shed for our sins bridges the gulf between a God infinitely far away from us in judgment and a God infinitely near to us in mercy.

20. The Hebrew for *glory* means "to be heavy, to have weight, to carry significance or to have importance." The word is first used in Genesis 12:10, "the famine was *severe* in the land." The next occurrence is in Genesis 13:2, "Abram was very *rich*."

21. Stephen Hawking and George Ellis, *The Large Scale Structure of Space-Time* (Cambridge: Cambridge University Press, 1973), p. 134.

22. Richard Gott, "Implications of the Copernican Principle for Our Future Prospects," *Nature* 363 (27 May 1993): 315–319.

23. Cited in Phillip E. Johnson, *Objections Sustained: Subversive Essays on Evolution, Law & Culture* (Downers Grove, IL: InterVarsity Press, 1998), p. 17.

because of the choice of a purposeful God, the "Divine Foot"—and thus it would be unlikely we are in a "special place."

Second, the cosmos has expanded. Both camps, evolutionary scientists and the Bible, articulate this. This expansion explains why astronomers observe galactic red shifts.[24]

The bounded/unbounded assumption is of profound importance. If you input the assumption that the material universe is unbounded into Albert Einstein's general theory of relativity equations, the output is the "Big Bang" cosmogony[25] with its attendant billions of years for the age of the universe. What is the destiny of the universe given the unbounded assumption? The universe will ultimately, after billions and billions of years, result in a Big Squash. If you input the assumption that the material universe is bounded into the same equations, the output is what D. Russell Humphreys calls the "Young-Earth Relativistic" cosmogony.[26] What is the destiny of the universe given the bounded assumption? All creation will ultimately, at some God-appointed time in the future, be reconciled in and through Christ (Colossians 1:19–20).

What are the purposes of the heavenly bodies?

> Then God said, "Let there be lights in the firmament of the heavens to divide the day from the night, and let them be for signs and seasons, and for days and years; and let them be for lights in the firmament of the heavens to give light on the earth"; and it was so. And God made the two great lights, the greater light to rule the day, and the lesser light to rule the night. *He made the stars also* (Genesis 1:14–16).

> He counts the number of the stars; He calls them all by name. Great *is* our Lord, and mighty in power; His understanding *is* infinite (Psalm 147:4–5).

> Lift up your eyes on high, and see who has created these *things*, who brings out their host by number; He calls them all by name, by the greatness of His might and the strength of *His* power; Not one is missing (Isaiah 40:26).

> *There is* one glory of the Sun, another glory of the Moon, and another glory of the stars; for *one* star differs from *another* star in glory (I Corinthians 15:41).

Our biblical and scientific understanding of the stars reveals the power, the might, the knowledge, the purpose, and the wonder of the Creator God. It is He who made the stars and put them in their heavenly heights. It is He who counts the stars. It is He who has a name for each, all 10^{26} of them!

The Bible says more about the purpose of the stars than their scientific makeup. Yes, the stars are gigantic atomic furnaces. If we stop at scientific definition, however, we will fail to see what God intends for us to see. C. S. Lewis (1898–1963), distinguished professor of Medieval and Renaissance literature at Cambridge University, wrote more than thirty books in his lifetime. In his famous Space Trilogy series, he attempted, using his unique gifts, to expose the errors of radical materialism (i.e., stars are *just* gigantic atomic furnaces) with its concomitant cosmic impersonalism:

> But Ransom, as time wore on, became aware of another and more spiritual cause for his progressive lightening and exultation of heart. A nightmare, long engendered in the modern mind by the mythology that follows in the wake of science, was falling off him. He had read of "Space": at the back of his thinking for years had lurked the dismal fancy of the black, cold vacuity, the utter deadness, which was supposed to separate the worlds. He had not known

---

24. The wavelengths of light from each galaxy are shifted toward the red side of the electromagnetic spectrum by a factor proportional to the distance of the galaxy from us. Astronomers have calculated this red shift and it is seems to indicate that distant galaxies are moving away from us at speeds approaching the speed of light.

25. Cosmogony refers to the study of ideas about the *origin* and *generation* of the universe. In contrast, cosmology is a study of the nature of the observable universe; i.e. how the universe *presently works*. Modern scientists sometimes cloud the difference between these two concepts.

26. See the excellent technical discussion of these issues in his book, *Starlight and Time*. The author acknowledges that many of the ideas presented in the previous section have been culled from this book by Humphreys.

how much it affected him till now—now that the very name "Space" seemed a blasphemous libel for this empyrean[27] ocean of radiance in which they swam. He could not call it "dead"; he felt life pouring into him from it every moment. How indeed should it be otherwise, since out of this ocean the worlds and all their life had come? He had thought it barren: he saw now that it was the womb of worlds, whose blazing and innumerable offspring looked down nightly even upon the earth with so many eyes—and here, with how many more! No: Space was the wrong name. Older thinkers had been wiser when they named it simply the heavens—the heavens which declare the glory....[28]

Scripture lays down the general principles on which the investigation of the stars must rest. Scripture provides a true framework for interpreting the facts. Knowing these Scriptural perspectives enables the Christian to pursue the knowledge of the stars in a way that honors and glorifies his or her Creator. With this in mind, we will study Genesis 1:14–16 which reveals five purposes of the heavenly lights—*lights, signs, seasons, days and years*, and *governing the day and the night*.

By way of introduction, it is important to understand that Old Testament Hebrew often employs a literary method called *chiasm*. Instead of listing related ideas in a logical sequence (Greek method), the Hebrews often related ideas in a sandwiched fashion. For example, the Greeks would say: Statement A relates to statement B. Statement C relates to statement D. Statement E relates to statement F. The Greek way of relating the ideas of Genesis 1:14 and 16 would be as follows, "The stars are for signs, the lesser light for seasons,

Figure 1–4: Chiastic Structure of Genesis 1:14 & 16

A	14. Let them be for signs
C	14. and for seasons
E	14. and for days and years
F	16. the greater light to govern the day
D	16. the lesser light to govern the night
B	16. He made the stars also

and the greater light for days and years." The Hebrews would say: Statements A, C, and E relate to statements F, D, and B. Genesis 1:14 and 16 uses this device: Signs (Statement A) are associated with the stars (Statement B). The seasons (Statement C) are associated with the lesser light, the Moon (Statement D), and the days and years (Statement E) are associated with the greater light, the Sun (Statement F).

Lights

First, the astral bodies are *lights*. Light in Scripture is a symbol of the nature of God (I John 1:5). Light points to beauty, purity, and holiness. Song of Solomon 6:10 says, "Who is this that grows like the dawn, as beautiful as the Full Moon, as pure as the Sun, as awesome as an army with banners?" Paul's first epistle to the Corinthians speaks of the uniqueness of the stars in their glory (I Corinthians 15:41). Glory here speaks of brilliance, outshining radiance, and awesome significance. Modern science has gifted biblical Christians with the ability to inspect the starry wonders in closer detail. Using the telescope, we can discern more of the glorious handiwork of our Creator. As we investigate deep sky wonders such as star clusters, galaxies, nebulae, and novas, we marvel at our Creator's ingenuity.

---

27.   The highest reaches of heaven, believed by the ancients to be a realm of pure fire or light; the abode of God and the angels; e.g., paradise.

28.   C. S. Lewis, *Out of the Silent Planet* (New York: Scribner, 1996), p. 32. For more on the ramifications of cosmic impersonalism, see Gary North, *The Dominion Covenant: Genesis* (Tyler, TX: Institute for Christian Economics, 1987), pp. 1–11.

Signs

Second, they are *signs*. A sign points to someone or something. In ancient times, signs were used as a witness of a special covenant either between God and mankind or between different peoples on the earth (see Genesis 9:12–13; Exodus 31:16–17; Joshua 24:25–27; I Samuel 7:12). In the Hebrew, the word "sign" could mean a map that gives directions that point to "Him who comes." Psalm 19 and Romans 10 confirm this:

> So then faith *comes* by hearing, and hearing by the word of God. But I say, have they not heard? Yes indeed: Their sound has gone out to all the earth and their words to the ends of the world (Romans 10:17–18).

In Psalm 19:1–4 we see the Psalmist David detailing the fact that the heavens, in their own unique way, are an inscription[29] of the glory of God.[30] Their firmament stands out and boldly manifests His handiwork—the work of His strength and power. Every day bubbles forth[31] poetic word and each night breathes out[32] intelligent understanding. There is no poetic word or speech where their extensive voice is not heard. Their outline[33] has gone out through all the earth even to the end of the world. This outline, this speech, is something that you can see with the eye. This speech is poetry in pictures, the only speech that everyone in the entire world could understand. Paul, in detailing the wondrous gospel of Christ, says that faith comes by hearing, and hearing by this gospel; i.e., the word of God. Then, he quotes from Psalm 19:4 proving that the ends of the world have already heard this word concerning the gospel in the heavens.[34] The word of God in the gospel can be "heard" by gazing into the night sky. Since the entire world has seen this rev-

Figure 1–5: Chiastic Structure of Psalm 19:1–2

Verse 1 — The testimony of the heavens

A   The heavens

    C   declare

        E   the glory of God;

        F   His handiwork.

    D   shows

B   And the firmament

Verse 2 — The testimony is continuous

A   Day unto day

    C   utters

        E   speech,

        F   and knowledge.

    D   reveals

B   And night unto night

---

29. The Hebrew for *declare* ("inscribe") means "to cut into, to engrave like letters on stone, or to write." It is also used for the concept of counting (Genesis 15:5) or narrating (Genesis 24:66).
30. Psalm 19 deals with God's revelation in creation (v. 1–6) and through His written word—His law (v. 7–14). These two revelations are complementary. The wrath of God abides upon all mankind, because they have suppressed the knowledge of God revealed in His created order (see Romans 1:18–32). God's revelation of Himself in creation is sufficient to condemn mankind in sin. This revelation will be corrupted by man and man can only come to a truthful understanding of God's creation through: (1) regeneration—the new birth (John 3:1–7) and (2) submission to God's written word as the basis for understanding His created order (Proverbs 1:7; 9:10; Psalm 36:9).
31. The Hebrew for *utter* ("bubbles up") is translated elsewhere as "to prophesy."
32. The Hebrew for *reveals* ("breathes out") literally means "to breathe."
33. The Hebrew for *line* ("outline") means "measuring line." This is a metonymy (a figure of speech in which one word or phrase is substituted for another with which it is closely associated). A carpenter uses a measuring line to mark out his work. According to H. F. W. Gesenius' (1786–1842) *Hebrew Lexicon*, it is a stylus or engraver with which an artist sketches the outlines of a figure that is later to be sculptured (see Isaiah 44:13). The stylus or outline of God's glory can be seen in the heavens. The sculpture that it points to is the written word (the law) of God (Psalm 19:7–11) embodied in the Lord Jesus Christ.
34. Christ is the glory of God manifested in the flesh (John 1:14).

elation, it is without excuse. The revelation of God in Christ, the reality to which the shadows of the sky point, is to be proclaimed in all the world by the beautiful feet of God's appointed preachers (Romans 10:14–15).[35]

God designed the stars not only as a sign pointing to His Son, but also as a sign pointing to the heavenly host. This host consists of the angelic (Job 38:7) and human (Philippians 2:15; Ephesians 2:6) assembly of vice-rulers under the one true Ruler of the universe. Stars also are linked to earthly rulers or nations. We shall look further into this subject shortly.

Seasons

Third, the heavenly lights exist to mark the *seasons.* As noted above, the Moon, or lesser light, exists particularly to mark the seasons. By seasons, we do not mean spring, summer, autumn, and winter. The Moon does not denote these seasons. The Hebrews used a lunar calendar that consisted of twelve months, each month consisting of about 29.5 days.[36] Each month began with each new Moon (visible crescent). In the Old Testament, the Moon particularly designated the feasts of the Lord (II Chronicles 8:13). The Moon marked the first day (new Moon) and the fifteenth day of the month (Full Moon). During Nisan (our

Figure 1–5: Chiastic Structure of Psalm 19:3–4

Verse 3 & 4 — The testimony is universal

A		[There is] no speech		
	C		nor language	
	D		[Where] their voice	
B		is not heard.		
A		Their line		
	C		has gone out	
		E		through all the earth,
		F		to the end of the world.
	D		*(understood)*	
B		And their words		

March-April), the Hebrews celebrated the Passover feast. On the fifteenth day of this month, they celebrated the Feast of Unleavened Bread (Leviticus 23:4–8). Seven Sabbaths (fifty days) after the Passover (Leviticus 23:15–16), they celebrated the Feast of Pentecost (or Weeks), during Sivan (our May-June). During Tishri (our September-October), the Feast of Trumpets began on the first day (Numbers 29:1–6; Psalm 81:3). On the fifteenth day of this month, the Feast of Tabernacles began (Leviticus 23:34–36).

The Moon governs the night (Psalm 136:9). In relationship to the Messianic purposes of God, the entire Old Testament occurred in the "night." Malachi, the last book of the night, foretold the coming "day of the Lord."

> For behold, the day is coming, burning like an oven; and all the proud, yes, all who do wickedly will be stubble. And the day which is coming shall burn them up, says the Lord of hosts, That will leave them neither root nor branch. But to you who fear My name the Sun of righteousness shall arise with healing in His wings; and you shall go out and grow fat like stall-fed calves (Malachi 4:1–2).

35. A missionary once told this story to Dr. Duane Edward Spencer of Grace Bible School. He had been speaking to a group of Japanese about the gospel—how Christ had come to die on the Cross, to shed His blood for His people's sins, to rise again from that place of death, and to shed forth His Holy Spirit to indwell His people. At the close of the meeting, an old woman came up to the missionary and said, "I'm so glad to have been here tonight. I've known this story since I was a child. It is all written in the names of the stars; but I never knew His name—the name Jesus—before" (abstracted from a tape recording of Barry Setterfield, *Exploring the Stars* (Sunnybank, Queensland, Australia: Creation Science Foundation Ltd., n.d.). The written word of God explains the reality of what the star names only point to in shadow.

36. This is the period required for the Moon to make a single revolution with respect to the Sun; it is called a synodic month.

Figure 1–6: The equinoxes and the solstices

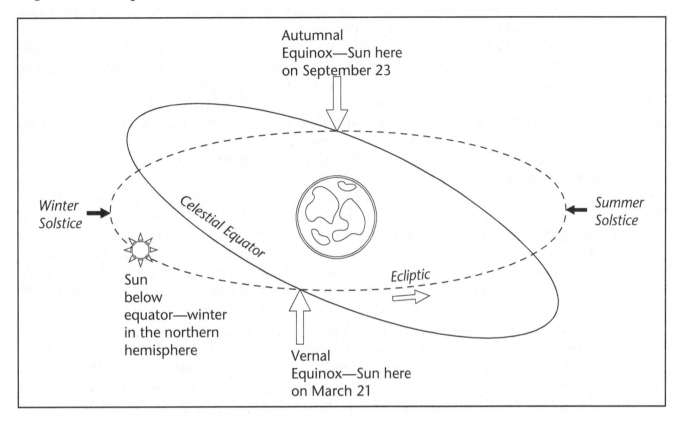

In the New Testament, the festival times have been fulfilled in Christ (Colossians 2:16–17). We are no longer obligated to keep the lunar regulatory feasts because the Sun of righteousness has risen in the person of Christ, the Light of the world.

Days and Years

Fourth, the Sun regulates *days and years*. Mankind's original clock could be seen daily in the sky. The position of the Sun, solar equinoxes[37] and solstices[38], and the precession (see Appendix Eleven) of Earth's axis helped ancient peoples mark the days and years.

Governing the Day and the Night

Fifth, the astral bodies emphasize *government* or rule. The Moon rules the night and the Sun rules the day. The governmental role of the astral bodies symbolizes earthly governments. Church leaders are symbolized by the stars (Revelation 1:20). Ungodly, apostate church rulers are symbolized as "wandering stars" (Jude 13). In Genesis 37:9, Joseph dreamt about the Sun, Moon, and stars bowing down to him. These astral bodies represented his brothers, tribal rulers in Israel. It is not an accident that most countries today use the Sun, Moon, and stars on their national flags. These astral bodies symbolize their respective governments.

---

37. An equinox occurs when the path of the Sun crosses the Celestial Equator (see Chapter Three). At this time, day and night are of equal length all over the Earth. The beginning of spring and autumn are denoted by the solar equinox.
38. A solstice occurs when the Sun is at its greatest distance from the Celestial Equator (see Chapter Three). Because of the precession of the Earth's axis, this maximum distance is 23.5°. This is the time of the longest day of the year in summer and the shortest day of the year in winter.

How are the stars and earthly rulers connected?

The Sun, ruler of the day, symbolizes the Lord God (Psalm 84:11). When the apostle John saw the risen and enthroned Christ, His face was shining like the Sun (Revelation 1:16). Earthly rulers can attempt to subvert the authority of the Christ, the Anointed One (Psalm 2). Throughout the Old Testament we see celestial and angelic government over the nations of men. The gods of these various nations are not to be dismissed as empty superstitions—they are real. The Apostle Paul understood the worship of these idolatrous gods as the worship of demons (I Corinthians 10:20). Associated with the idols of the Old Testament nations were fallen angels who, in opposition to God yet under control by God, exercised control over these nations.

For example, Pharaoh of Egypt claimed to be the incarnation of the Sun god, Ra. In Daniel 10:12–14, Michael, an archangel (compare with Revelation 12:7 and Jude 9), is identified as one of the chief princes and is connected, in some authentic way, to the rulership of God's people, the nation of Israel. We also read of a spiritual entity, also a prince, connected to the kingdom of Persia. This unnamed prince withstood Michael for twenty-one days. The lamentation for the King of Tyre in Ezekiel 28:11–16 is spoken to the King as if he were *in Eden*, the garden of God, and an anointed cherub![39] The King of Tyre was a man, not a cherub and lived in Tyre, not in Eden. What is important to note is that this King is linked to a cherub; a cherub whose history is not only entwined with the events of Eden, but also is connected with the history of the kingdom of Tyre.

> Among the gods *there is* none like You, O Lord; nor *are there any works* like Your works. All nations whom You have made shall come and worship before You, O Lord, and shall glorify Your Name. For You *are* great, and do wondrous things; You alone *are* God (Psalm 86:8–10).

The Bible takes these beings, or gods, seriously, but not in the sense that they can be victorious in a war against God. They are creatures under the direct control of their Creator. The one, true God has given to these princes, in some limited sense, mediatorial rule over the destiny of nations.[40]

The New Testament tells us that God has established Christ as the one, true Sovereign—the Prince of life, the Ruler of the kings of the earth, the King of kings and Lord of lords (Acts 3:15; Revelation 1:5; 19:16). The new age inaugurated by the coming of Christ is identified in the New Testament as the "age or world to come" (Hebrews 6:5). In Hebrews 2, the writer is quoting Psalm 8, a Psalm restating the dominion mandate given to man:

> For He has not put the world to come, of which we speak, in subjection to angels. But one testified in a certain place, saying, "What is man that You are mindful of him, or the son of man that You take care of him? You have made him a little lower than the angels; you have crowned him with glory and honor, and set him over the works of Your hands. You have put all things in subjection under his feet." For in that He put all in subjection under him, He left nothing that is not put under him. But now we do not yet see all things put under him. But we see Jesus, who was made a little lower than the angels, for the suffering of death crowned with glory and honor, that He, by the grace of God, might taste death for everyone (Hebrews 2:5–9).

We see that the world to come or the age inaugurated by the coming of Christ is not subjected to angels (as in the Old Testament) but to the *dominion of man in Christ*. We do not yet see all things put under man in Christ (there is more work to do as this first century writer noted), but we do see Jesus to whom God has given universal dominion over all things (including angels). God has always exercised sovereign control over everything. What this passage in Hebrews is talking about is that, in the Old Testament, God mediated His control over the world through the tutelage of angels or princes (some fallen, others not). In Christ, God has disposed of the old system of mediatorial princes and now there is one mediator between God and man, the man Christ Jesus (I Timothy 2:5).

---

39.   In Hebrew, a *cherub* is a being of sublime and celestial nature. It literally means "powerful, strong, majestic." The by-product of viewing such a being, whether godly or ungodly, would be nothing less than "frightful horror."

40.   See Charles Hodges insight on angels in Chapter XIII of his *Systematic Theology*, Vol. I (New York: Charles Scribner's Sons, 1906), pp. 637–648.

Christians now live in the "age to come"—where God has established His mediatorial rule in the Prince of Life, Jesus Christ.

What does this have to do with the stars and earthly rulership? The Old Testament prophets announced God's judgment on particular nations using the imagery of a collapsing universe where "Sun, Moon, and stars fall to Earth." How are we to understand this? As mere symbol, or something more?

Note the confession of the King of Babylon and how he is described as Lucifer[41] (another prince):

> I will ascend into heaven, I will exalt my throne above the stars of God (Isaiah 14:13).

We need to read this passage in the same way as we have read Ezekiel 28. The King of Babylon was a man, not Lucifer. Again, this King is linked to Lucifer; a prince whose history is not only entwined with the events of history past, but also is connected with the history of the kingdom of Babylon—by enticing the King of Babylon to do something that he once tried to do. Note how this aspiration should not be ruled out as impossible. Daniel describes the growth of the power of Antiochus Epiphanes[42] in *very similar language*:

> And it grew up to the host of heaven; and it cast down *some* of the host and *some* of the stars to the ground, and trampled them. He even exalted *himself* as high as the Prince of the host; and by him the daily *sacrifices* were taken away, and the place of His sanctuary was cast down (Daniel 8:10–11).

Note also the link between the host of heaven and the destruction of Sisera in the book of Judges:

> They fought from the heavens; the stars from their courses fought against Sisera (Judges 5:20).

The prophet Isaiah links the powers of the heavens with the kings of the earth in the following passage:

> It shall come to pass in that day *that* the Lord will punish on high the host of exalted ones, and on the earth the kings of the earth. They will be gathered together, as prisoners are gathered in the pit and will be shut up in the prison; after many days they will be punished (Isaiah 24:21–22).

It is in this context that we are to understand the "collapsing universe" terminology that we will explore next. The prophets associated the universe dissolving with God's judgment of various nations. Not only did God judge these nations in a political sense (i.e., removing them from history), He also judged their governing celestial prince (indicated by the "falling stars" terminology) by causing them also to "fall from power."

Note the words of the prophet Isaiah:

> Behold, the day of the Lord comes, Cruel, with both wrath and fierce anger, to lay the land desolate; and He will destroy its sinners from it. For the *stars* of heaven and their constellations will not give their light; the *sun* will be darkened in its going forth, and the *moon* will not cause its light to shine (Isaiah 13:9–10).

In verse one we find the object of Isaiah's oracle, "The burden against Babylon." The entire chapter deals with the termination of Babylon, even detailing that God will use the Medes as instruments of judgment (Isaiah 13:17). The Sun and Moon will stop functioning. Their clocks are going to stop. Time has run out. Their stars (princely rulers) are going to be extinguished. Note that the prince of Babylon enticed this civilization to practice astrology, the worship of the heavens. God darkened what they worshipped.

---

41. Amazingly, Lucifer means "brightness" or "morning star." Christ is also depicted as the "morning star" (Revelation 2:28; 22:16).

42. *Epiphanes* means "manifest god." He reigned over Palestine in the second century B.C. desecrating the Jewish temple in 165 B.C. The Jews likened him to be a "mad man."

Figure 1–7: Chiastic Structure of Acts 2:16–21

Verse 16

A But this is what was spoken by the prophet Joel: And it shall come to pass

Verses 17-18

  C in the last days

    E that I will pour out of My Spirit

      G on all flesh

        I Your sons and your daughters shall prophesy

          K your young men shall see visions

          L your old men shall dream dreams

        J and they shall prophesy

      H And on My menservants and on My maidservants

    F I will pour out of My Spirit

  D in those days

Verses 19-21a

    E' I will show

      G' wonders in the heaven above

        I' and signs on the earth beneath:

        J' blood and fire and vapor of smoke.

      H' The sun shall be turned into darkness, and the moon into blood

    F' before the coming of the great and awesome day of the Lord.

Verse 21b

B And it shall come to pass that whoever calls on the name of the Lord shall be saved

In Ezekiel 32:7–8, the prophet describes the lamentation of the prophet against Pharaoh, king of Egypt. He uses the same imagery Your stars darkened, the Sun covered with a cloud (compare with Exodus 10:21–23), and the Moon's light smothered. The Egyptians worshipped the Sun god, Ra. God darkened what they worshipped.

God pronounces judgment on His own people, Israel, using similar imagery in the book of Joel. In the first two chapters, Joel describes the invasion of insect and human locusts. He proclaims this message: the "day of the Lord is coming" (Joel 2:1). The light of God's rising day always exposes the darkness of sin. The "Day of the Lord" in Scripture always refers to His coming in judgment to deal with national sins. There were many such "Days of the Lord" in the Old Testament.

Spoken on the first day of the Feast of Pentecost (about A.D. 30), Peter quoted Joel's remarks about wonders in the sky above and signs on earth (Acts 2:19–20). In reverse order (chiasm), the signs on the earth include blood, fire, and vapor of smoke. These phrases speak of the horrors of war. This came to pass when the Romans invaded Palestine and destroyed the city of Jerusalem in A.D. 70. This is the shaking that the writer of Hebrews referred to in Hebrews 12:25–29.

The wonders in the sky above relate to the Sun turning black, a solar eclipse, and the Moon turning blood red. Using prophetic imagery, this verse does not speak of a general physical darkening of the skies; it speaks of an eclipse of a nation. Blood speaks of the sacrificial system of the Old Testament. Apostate Israel, in rejecting the saving blood of Jesus, became blood sacrifices themselves during the Roman invasion of Jerusalem.[43] Because the Jewish nation continued the sacrificial system, an abomination in the sight of God, God made the nation a bloody sacrifice of judgment; their Moon (symbol of the Feast days) turned into blood.

There is a way of escape, however: Call upon the name of the Lord! (Acts 2:21). Those who put their trust in the blood of the Lamb of God, the final and only acceptable sacrifice, escaped the destruction of Jerusalem in A.D. 70. Josephus documents that no Christians lost their lives in this war.

Joel continues his prophetic word by saying that "the *sun* and *moon* will grow dark, and the *stars* will diminish their brightness" (Joel 3:15). In context, this speaks of God bringing all the nations to a day of decision: Will they follow the one, true God or continue in their sinful, rebellious ways? In this sense, God shakes the nations (compare with Haggai 2:6–7 with Hebrews 12:26) causing their governments to tremble at His voice of judgment. The only true refuge will be the Lord Himself (Joel 3:16–17). The nations that respond to this shaking will experience beauty and blessings from the Living God pictured as the sweet wine and flowing milk (Joel 3:18–21).

Speaking of the destruction of Jerusalem, Jesus said that "immediately after the tribulation of those days, the *sun* will be darkened, and the *moon* will not give its light, and the *stars* will fall from heaven, and the powers of the heavens will be shaken" (Matthew 24:29).[44] After God judged Jerusalem, He continued (and continues to this very day) to shake all the other nations. His earthly host, messengers of the gospel of Christ, continued to proclaim the light of His purposes to all the nations. Through this gospel proclamation, God shakes the nations, removes the squatter princes,[45] and replaces them with the light of the Sun of Righteousness, whose rising brings healing to the nations (Malachi 4:2; Revelation 22:2).

Why study the stars?

First, we study the stars because they speak to us concerning the wondrous attributes and purposes of their Creator (Romans 1:20–21). Every time we look at the night sky, a godly hush and awe should overcome us.

Second, we study the stars because great men of faith studied them. Abraham (Genesis 15:5), Job (Job 38:31–33), and David (Psalm 8; 19) all studied the stars and drew inspiration from them.

---

43. See Flavius Josephus, *The Jewish War*, ed. Gaalya Cornfield (Grand Rapids: Zondervan Publishing House, 1982).
44. See also Mark 13:24–25, Luke 21:24–26, and Revelation 6:13; 8:12. All of these passages speak of this historical judgment of God on Jerusalem in A.D. 70.
45. In the light of Christ's enthronement, these princes have not been destroyed, only plundered in terms of their authority over the nations (see Matthew 12:28–29 and Revelation 20:1–3). They are like squatters in that they no longer have legal claim on the nations. It is the mission of the Church, through the power of the Gospel (Matthew 28:18–20), to evict these "squatter princes" from realms they have no right to claim. This is the essence of spiritual warfare (Ephesians 6:12).

Third, we study the stars because they are symbols revealing to us: (1) the word concerning Christ and (2) the word concerning the heavenly host and earthly rulers.

It is the purpose of the rest of this book to detail for you the word concerning Christ seen in the night sky.[46] Therefore, as we approach the study of the stars, we are not following the ways of the ungodly. Ungodly scientists study the night sky for purely materialistic reasons. They deny the reality of the Creator God and can go no farther than measurement and mystery. Other people look at the night sky for directions for their lives. Countless millions of people are slaves to the horoscope charts believing that through them they can receive guidance.

The biblical Christian looks at the night sky and sees the handiwork of his Creator and Redeemer. The biblical Christian sees in the stars a map pointing to Christ, the true source of direction and guidance. The biblical Christian looks to the glorious light of God that the stars represent, is transformed by it, and brings that light to nations bound in the darkness of sin.

Figure 1–8: Chiastic Structure of Isaiah 60:1–3

A   Arise, shine

    C   for your light has come

        E   And the glory of the Lord is risen upon you

            G   For behold, the darkness shall cover the earth

            H   and deep darkness the people

        F   But the Lord will arise over you, and His glory will be seen upon you

    D   The Gentiles [nations] shall come to your light

B   and kings to the brightness of your rising

---

46.   For the star name meanings the author has relied primarily on the work of E. W. Bullinger, *The Witness of the Stars*. Bullinger based his studies upon Miss Frances Rolleston's *Mazzaroth or The Constellations* (1863). Richard Hinkley Allen, in *Star Names: Their Lore and Meaning* (New York: Dover Publications, 1963 [1899]), considered Rolleston's work to be "especially remarkable" (p. 28). The interpretation and application of these star name meanings will be governed by the theological and doctrinal commitments of the commentator. Understanding this, the reader is advised that the author's interpretation and application will occasionally differ from Bullinger.

Questions for Review and Further Study

Short sentence answers:

1. Define the following words:

   a. Star

   b. Lucid star

   c. Radio star

   d. Scientific notation

   e. Parallax

   f. Astronomical unit

   g. Light-year

   h. Galactic red shift

   i. Gravitational time dilation

   j. Cosmogony

   k. Cosmology

   l. Solstice

   m. Equinox

   n. Chiasm

2. List the five purposes of the heavenly bodies according to Genesis 1:14–16.

Long Essay:

1. How would you respond to the following statement, "How can you believe in a recent act of creation, some 6,000 to 10,000 years ago, when science has shown that some galaxies are more than one million light-years distant from Earth?"

2. Explain how the phases of the Moon correspond to the Old Testament feasts.

3. Carefully explain and relate Psalm 19:1–4 to Romans 10:17–18.

4. Write a newspaper article explaining the fall of ancient Babylon using the Old Testament imagery found in Isaiah 13.

5. Write a newspaper article explaining the fall of a modern nation in the light of Old Testament imagery.

Research:

Do a research project on one of the following:

1. The work of astronomer Barry Setterfield and the decreasing speed of light theory.

2. The work of physicist D. Russell Humphreys and the Young-Earth Relativistic cosmogony.

Chapter Two

North Circumpolar Stars

This chapter deals with North Circumpolar[47] Stars—stars seen from Earth's Northern Hemisphere as you look north. They are observed ideally from North America, Europe, North Africa, and most of Asia.

We will identify and comment on these stars as they appear in their appropriate constellations. A constellation is a group of stars that form pictures in the sky that speak of the Gospel of Christ. Among other sights, two beautiful constellations embellish the northern sky. They are the Big Dipper and the Little Dipper.

Big and Little Dippers

The Big and Little Dippers are popular names for Ursa Major and Ursa Minor. The brightest stars in these constellations form what looks like long-handled utensils. Ursa Major means "Great Bear" and Ursa Minor means "Little Bear." The bear pictures are probably perversions, as the following analysis suggests.

Ursa Minor

The Hebrews called Ursa Minor *Dobher*, meaning "fold" like in sheepfold. Dohver is very similar to Dobheh (means "rest or security") and Dobh (means "bear"). From this, it is clear how the bear picture could have come about. The most important, and brightest, star of Ursa Minor is Al Ruccaba (means "the turned or ridden on") or Polaris, the North Star.

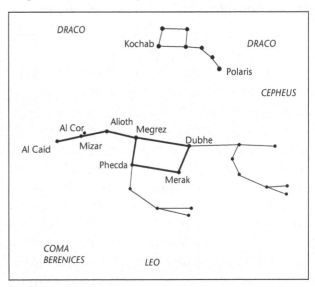

Figure 2–1: Ursa Major and Ursa Minor

The brightest star in a constellation is scientifically identified by the prefix *alpha* (see Appendix One). So, Polaris is also known as Alpha Ursae Minoris.[48] Scientists use a measuring system called magnitude to express the apparent brightness of stars (See Appendices Three and Four). Two Greek astronomers, Hipparchus (190?–120 B.C.) and Ptolemy (ca. A.D. 90–168), inaugurated this system.

---

47. *Circumpolar* refers to celestial bodies that never set and therefore are always seen from a given location on Earth.
48. *Ursae Minoris* is the genitive form of the constellation name.

They noted the twenty brightest stars in the sky and grouped them together as stars of the "first magnitude." Stars about 2.5 times fainter were classified as stars of the "second magnitude." Those 2.5 times fainter than second magnitude stars were classified as stars of the "third magnitude," and so on. Stars of the sixth magnitude were at the limit of naked-eye visibility. This system, virtually unaltered, is still in use today. Astronomers have set 2.512 as the exact ratio between magnitudes. When the difference in magnitude between two stars is five, it means one star is one hundred times brighter than the other; i.e., a star of magnitude one is one hundred times brighter than a star of magnitude six. Mathematically, the magnitude scale is logarithmic (2.512 is the fifth root of one hundred). Polaris has a magnitude of 1.99 (forty-ninth brightest star in the sky[49]) and is 782 light-years away.

The color of Polaris is yellow-white. Scientists can calculate the estimated temperature of a star by its color. Telescopes receive light from a star passing it through a special prism. This prism splits the light into the colors of the spectrum. By studying this spectrum, scientists can discover many things about the stars, one of which is their temperature (see Appendix Six). The spectral analysis of Polaris suggests it to be a "lukewarm" star with a temperature of approximately 7,500°K.[50]

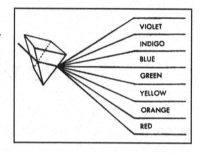

Figure 2–2: The Spectrum

VIOLET
INDIGO
BLUE
GREEN
YELLOW
ORANGE
RED

Polaris is also a double or binary star. This means that Polaris has a sister star (of pale bluish tint and magnitude of 9) quite close and both revolve about each other. It was first seen by Sir William Herschel (1738–1822), a German-born British astronomer who also discovered the planet Uranus, in 1780. This binary arrangement is quite common. Possibly half the stars are double or multiple system stars.

In many cultures, this star has been seen as a symbol of faithfulness. For example, John Keats, in his *Last Sonet*, writes, "Bright star! Would I were steadfast as thou art...." And William Shakespeare has Julius Caesar confess, moments before his assassination, "... but I am constant as the northern star...."

The Old Testament suggests a link between God's holy mountain and the northern sky or possibly the northern stars. Note the following:

> He comes from the north as golden *splendor*; with God is awesome majesty (Job 37:22).

> Great *is* the Lord, and greatly to be praised in the city of our God, *in* His holy mountain, beautiful in elevation, the joy of the whole earth, *is* Mount Zion on the sides of the north, the city of the great King (Psalm 48:1–2).

The phrase "sides of the north" literally means "beyond Zaphon." This same word is used in Isaiah's oracle against the degenerate monarch of Babylon, comparing him with the fallen angel, Lucifer, "How you are fallen from heaven, O Lucifer, son of the morning! ... For you have said in your heart, 'I will ascend into heaven, I will exalt my throne above the stars of God; I will also sit on the mount of the congregation on the farthest sides of the north'" (Isaiah 14:11–13). Zaphon is a mountain often described in Canaanite texts as the dwelling place of *their* gods. Sumerian inscriptions mention a great peak called "the mountain of the world" in the far north. In a great many ancient cultures, we find this concept symbolized on land by some sort of "temple mountain"—the ziggurat in Babylon and Sumer, the pyramid in Egypt, the teocalli in Mexico. Could it be that these "north" and "mountain" indicators reflect in these cultures the vestige of the God of gods, the God of the Bible?

The prophet Ezekiel sees a vision of God through "a whirlwind coming out of the north" (Ezekiel 1:4; compare with Revelation 4). One final passage from the Psalms associates God with the north:

---

49.   Its luminosity is 1,600. That means it shines with the brightness of 1,600 Suns.
50.   *K* refers to an absolute scale of temperature based on kelvin (the base **SI unit*** of temperature, defined as 1/273.6 of the triple point of water); °K = °C + 273.
       *Refers to the unit of measurement established by the *Système International*.

For exaltation *comes* neither from the east nor from the west nor from the south. But God *is* the Judge: He puts down on, and exalts another (Psalm 75:6–7).

Here we see that God, the Judge, brings exaltation or debasement from the north—where He alone is exalted in glorious splendor. What we can conclude from these Scriptures is that somehow the majesty of God is associated with *north*. Let us remember this as we lift our eyes on high toward the north.

Polaris has been an invaluable guide to seamen for centuries[51] as a navigational guide for determining a ship's latitudinal position at sea (see Appendix Eight). Polaris now lies one degree[52] off truth north. In the year 2102 (when it will be at its closest), it will lie one-half degree away. Due to a phenomenon known as the precession of the axis, Thuban in Draco was the "North Star" during Abraham's time (see Appendix Eleven). As north stars slowly changed with the passing of millennia, we've never had one as bright *and* as close to true north as Polaris. There are 41,253 square degrees of sky, and only some 50 stars are as bright as or brighter than Polaris. The chances of such a noticeable star occupying this spot are nearly 1,000 to 1 against. This star is not there by chance, but by God's design and providence in order to further His eternal purposes.

In the early period of European exploration (fifteenth and sixteenth centuries), mariners considered Polaris as an indispensable navigational tool.[53] The need for better precision, i.e., determining one's longitude at sea, became a pressing problem that challenged the greatest scientific minds of the day.[54] In 1761, through the application of Hooke's law[55] and basic trigonometric functions, John Harrison (1693–1776), British horologist, invented the first practical marine chronometer.[56] This timepiece enabled navigators to compute accurately their longitude at sea to a fraction of a second. With this tool, the seas became much safer to navigate.

The Englishman John Hadley and the American Thomas Godfrey independently developed the sextant in 1731. With this instrument came increased precision in determining the altitude[57] of Polaris and other celestial bodies. Turned on its side, it could make precise angular measurements. In 1764, the British high command employed two Protestant refugees, Joseph Desbarres from France and Samuel Hollandt from Holland, to chart the eastern coast of America using a sextant turned on its side. In Canada, one of the pupils of Desbarres and Hollandt was a young naval officer named James Cook (1728–1779). He used this cartographic knowledge to map (and plant the British flag on) the coasts of New Zealand and Australia in the 1770s.

Figure 2–3: The Sextant

In 1792, William Carey (1761–1834) founded the first Protestant missionary society (Baptist Missionary Society) in 1792 and in the nineteenth century Christian missionaries spread the Gospel

---

51. Since the third century B.C., navigators have also called this star the *Lodestar* or *Steering Star*.
52. A convenient way to measure distances between celestial objects in the night sky is by degree measurement. One degree is about the width of the end of a person's little finger when the arm is held straight out. The degree measurement from horizon to zenith (the point on the Celestial Sphere that is directly above the observer) is 90°.
53. Why did this happen in Europe and why at this time? See James Nickel, *Mathematics: Is God Silent?* (Vallecito, CA: Ross House Books, 1990), pp. 31–48.
54. See Dava Sobel, *Longitude* (New York: Walker and Company, 1995).
55. Named for Robert Hooke (1635–1703), British scientist, who developed a formula that identified the quantitative relationship between the spring and the bob.
56. Harrison, whose singleness of purpose had made it possible for him to achieve what, to other scientists of his era (including Galileo and Sir Isaac Newton), was impossible, wrote, "I think I may make bold to say, that there is neither any other Mechanical or Mathematical thing in the World that is more beautiful or curious in texture than this my watch or Time-keeper for the Longitude … and I heartily thank Almighty God that I have lived so long, as in some measure to complete it." Cited in Rupert T. Gould, *The Marine Chronometer: Its History and Development* (London, 1923), p. 63.
57. The angular distance of a celestial object above the horizon.

around the world traveling on ships using these navigational aids. After Carey noted these aids, he said, "providence seems in a manner to invite us to the trial."[58]

The second brightest star in Ursa Minor is Beta Ursae Minoris or Kochab. Kochab means "waiting for Him who cometh." Its magnitude is 2.07 and is 104 light-years away. Gamma Ursae Minoris is also known as Al Pherkadain meaning "the redeemed assembly." The magnitude of this star is 3.04 and it lies 270 light-years away.

Ursa Major

The Arabs identified Ursa Major as Al Naish, meaning "the assembled together." Other cultures have called this constellation the Plough, Seven Wise Men, Seven Little Indians, the Heavenly Wain (wagon),[59] and Charles Wain.[60] Individual stars that form the "dipper" (called an *asterim*[61]) in this constellation, in rough order of brightness, are:

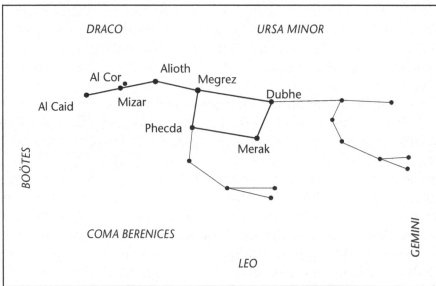

Figure 2–4: Ursa Major

1. Dubhe, Dubh, or Dubb (Alpha Ursae Majoris) meaning "flock" (magnitude of 1.79 at 104 light-years).

2. Merak, Merach, or Mirak (Beta Ursae Majoris) meaning "purchased flock" (magnitude of 2.37 at 78 light-years). The two stars, Dubhe and Merak, point the viewer to Polaris. Extend the distance between Merak and Dubhe six times beyond Dubhe and you will find Polaris.

3. Phaeda, Phad, Phacda, or Phecda (Gamma Ursae Majoris) meaning "visited, guarded, numbered" (magnitude of 2.44 at 90 light-years).

4. Megrez (Delta Ursae Majoris) meaning "tail" (magnitude of 3.30 at 63 light-years).

5. Alioth (Epsilon Ursae Majoris) meaning "she goat" (somewhat variable[62] magnitude of 1.78 at 82 light-years).

6. Mizar (Zeta Ursae Majoris) meaning "separate or small" (magnitude of 2.09 at 88 light-years). Mizar has a companion star of magnitude 4.02, Al Cor (80 Ursae Majoris), meaning "the lamb." Resolving these two stars with the naked eye is proof of excellent eyesight.

7. Benet Naish of Al Kaid (Eta Ursae Majoris) meaning "the daughters of the assembly or the assembled" (magnitude of 1.86 at 150 light-years).

58.　William Carey, "An Enquiry into the Obligation of Christians to Use Means for the Conversion of the Heathens," in *Perspectives on the World Christian Movement: A Reader,* ed. Ralph Winter and Steven Hawthorne (Pasadena, CA: William Carey Library, 1981), p. 233.

59.　Some medieval Christians pictured it as the heavenly chariot in which Elijah was taken up to heaven. Actually, he was not taken up to heaven in a chariot; it was a whirlwind (II Kings 2:1).

60.　Some older medieval English texts denote this constellation as Cherlemaynes Wayne and Charel-Wayne.

61.　An *asterim* is a pattern of stars within a constellation but not itself a constellation.

62.　A variable star varies in brightness with periods ranging from minutes to years.

The Big Dipper Clock

The Big Dipper rotates in a counterclockwise, circular motion around Polaris, which, as we have noted, is one degree away from the North Celestial Pole (N.C.P.). The N.C.P. is a point in the sky that is on a line that extends Earth's rotational axis. The South Circumpolar Stars rotate in a clockwise motion around an imaginary point in the night sky, called the South Celestial Pole (S.C.P.). Unfortunately, for those who live in the Southern Hemisphere, there is no star nearby the South Celestial Pole that suggests due south.

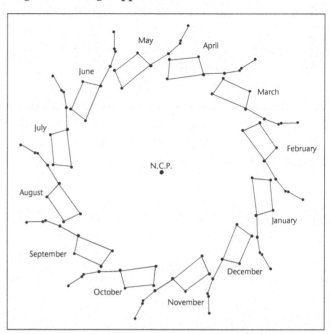

Figure 2–5: Big Dipper Clock

The motion of the Big Dipper during the night acts as a celestial time clock. As you face north, Figure 2–5 shows the relative positions of the Big Dipper as it would appear in mid-month throughout the year at 9 P.M. Each month is an hour indicator on our celestial clock. For example, May would be twelve o'clock, February would be three o'clock, November would be six o'clock, and August would be nine o'clock.

Every two hours, the Big Dipper moves the clock space of one hour. For example, if, during June, we look for the Big Dipper at 9 P.M., we will find it in the eleven o'clock position. Two hours later, at 11 P.M., the Big Dipper will be in the July, or ten o'clock, position. At 7 P.M. (two hours before the 9 P.M. position), the Big Dipper would be in the May, or twelve o'clock, position; that is, nearly upside down.

If we know the time of night, then we can find the month by reversing the above procedure. For example, the time is 11 P.M. and the Big Dipper is in the December, or five o'clock, position. What month is it? Two hours earlier, at 9 P.M., the Big Dipper would have been in the six o'clock position. The month is therefore November.

Figure 2–6: M101

You can see several beautiful spiral galaxies[63] by looking in the direction of Ursa Major. They are M81, M82, NGC[64] 2976, M101, and NGC 2841. The Owl Nebula,[65] M97, is a conspicuous deep sky object in this constellation. M81

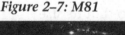
Figure 2–7: M81

and M82 are estimated to be 6.5 million light-years distant. M101 is 14 million light-years away and M97's distance is estimated at 10,000 light-years. To sight these requires a good telescope.[66]

63.　There are three different types (or classes) of galaxies: (1) Ellipticals, (2) Spirals, and (3) Irregulars. See Robert Burnham, Jr., *Burnham's Celestial Handbook*, vol. 1 (New York: Dover Publications, 1978), pp. 91–95.
64.　Refers to the *New General Catalogue* (NGC) which was compiled by John L. E. Dreyer in 1888.
65.　A *nebula* is a cloud of gas or dust in space.
66.　Telescopes come in three types: (1) refractors (use lenses to gather light), (2) reflectors (use mirrors to gather light), and (3) catadioptrics (use lenses and mirrors in combination to gather light).

Two "Naked-eye" Galaxies

There are two companion galaxies of our own (called the Milky Way) that can be seen with the naked eye.[67] One is a large irregular elliptical galaxy called the Large Magellanic Cloud (L.M.C.). It is 160,000 light-years away with dimensions of 12° by 4°. Its major, or long, axis is 30,000 light-years in length and it contains about 5×10^9 stars. The other is the Small Magellanic Cloud (S.M.C.). It is about half the diameter of the Large Magellanic Cloud and has about 1.5×10^9 stars. Its estimated distance is 190,000 light-years.

Both of these galaxies are located in the south circumpolar region. Only residents living in the Southern Hemisphere (e.g., Australia, New Zealand, South Africa, or South America) can see them. Portuguese seamen discovered them in the fifteenth century and they named them after their fellow-explorer Ferdinand Magellan.

Figure 2–8: The Milky Way (Top View)

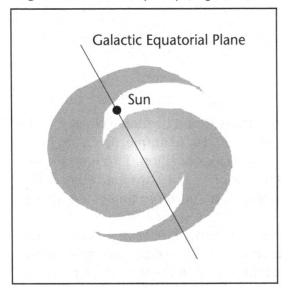

The Milky Way

The white band of light stretching across the entire night sky is the concentrated light coming from the dense conglomeration of stars located around the central axis of our galaxy, the Milky Way.

Viewed from above, the Milky Way's outline would appear circular, the stars forming a spiral, or pinwheel, design. A side view would reveal its thinness. At the center of the galaxy is a concentration of stars. Two arms start at opposite sides of the center and spiral about it. The diameter is estimated to be 100,000 light-years and the maximum thickness to be between 10,000 and 15,000 light-years.

Our Sun with its system of planets occupies a position about 30,000 light-years from the center and close to the galactic equatorial plane.

Let us shrink the Milky Way down so that its size covers the continental United States. The billions of stars would appear on the map as specks averaging about 200 yards apart. Our Solar System, if we could locate it, would be about two inches in diameter. The Sun and Earth would be about three hundredths of an inch apart.

Looking at this multitude of stars from our own small

Figure 2–9: The Milky way (Side View)

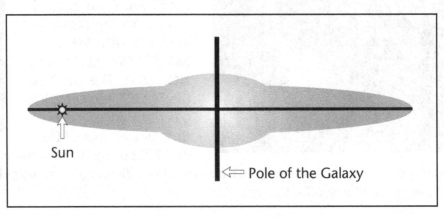

planet, one gets two distinct views. In the direction parallel to the pole of the galaxy, due to thinness of the latter, individual stars are seen against a dark background. The view along the equatorial plane is different in that the closer stars are seen against a faint luminous band (Milky Way). This

---

67.   The only other galaxy that can be seen with the naked eye is the Andromeda galaxy (M31).

band owes its existence to the merging light of the billions of stars present in the thick part of our galaxy. This band of light suggests the direction of the equatorial plane of our galaxy.

The shape of our galaxy implies that it is rotating. Its axis of rotation is perpendicular to the equatorial plane of the galaxy. All stars in the Milky Way do not rotate uniformly around its hub. The stars near the center of our galaxy move at great orbital velocities. Stars far from the center rotate at smaller velocities. Our Sun has an orbital velocity of about 150 miles per second. Stars close to the center seem to outrun the Sun while stars closer to the edge seem to move at slower speeds. A "galactic year" is the time it takes for our Sun to make one revolution—about 225,000,000 Earth years given its current orbital velocity.

Facts and Faith

Is the position of our Solar System in the Milky Way just happenstance? Or, has God designed its location just perfectly? Is Earth in Space by chance or by design?

We must recognize that the *faith* of a man or a culture will determine the answers to the above questions. All thinking is founded upon faith. The true facts about God's creation will be the same for the man of the Christian faith and any other faith. It is the frame of reference for understanding these facts that will be different.

Other words for *faith* are:

> **Presupposition:**   *Pre* means "before" and *supposition* means "belief without full evidence."

> **Premise:**   a proposition antecedently supposed (e.g., the axioms or postulates of Euclidean geometry).

> **Pre-commitment:**   a preliminary act or pledging of trust.

> **Paradigm:**   a model that provides a basis for understanding the facts.

Faith conditions the way the facts before us are understood and interpreted. Consider a fish and a submarine. The facts about both are that they have tails and navigate underwater. Consider two *faith* scenarios. First, assume that similarity equals common ancestry. When interpreting the facts by this faith, we conclude that the fish is a highly advanced, miniaturized great-nephew of the submarine. Second, assume that similarity equals a common designer. When interpreting the facts by this faith, we conclude that both were designed to work underwater; one by man, the other by God. Note that with the right *facts* but a wrong *faith* you can come up with the *wrong* answer for all the *right* reasons!

Philosopher and mathematician Alfred North Whitehead (1861–1947) said, "Theories are built upon facts; and conversely the reports upon facts are shot through and through with theoretical interpretation."[68] Paleontologist Stephen Jay Gould said, "Facts do not 'speak for themselves'; they are read in the light of theory."[69] In the context of discussing geocentricity and heliocentricity, astronomer Sir Fred Hoyle (1915–) said:

> Writers on scientific method usually tell us that scientific discoveries are made "inferentially," that is to say, from putting together many facts. But this is far from being correct. The facts by themselves are never sufficient to lead unequivocally to the really profound discoveries. Facts are always analyzed in terms of the prejudices of the investigator. The prejudices are of a deep kind, relating to our views on how the Universe "must" be constructed.[70]

Ideas have consequences. Research metallurgist Ian T. Taylor said "… presuppositions can not only make us see what does not exist but can also prevent us from seeing what does."[71] In July of

---

68.   Alfred North Whitehead, *Adventures of Ideas* (New York: The Free Press, 1967), p. 3.
69.   Stephen J. Gould, *Ever Since Darwin* (New York: W. W. Norton, 1977), p. 161.
70.   Fred Hoyle, *Highlights in Astronomy* (San Francisco: W. H. Freeman & Company, 1975), pp. 35–36.

1959, paleontologist Louis Leakey found a bit of a skull bone and two teeth in Nairobi, Kenya. He said, "We knelt together to examine this treasure … and cried with sheer joy. For years people had been telling us that we'd better stop looking, but I felt deep down that it had to be there. You must be patient about these things."[72] Note that Leakey knew what he found *before* he examined it; he was finding proof for a theory already accepted. The Piltdown man forgery is a classic case of how a few men, blinded by their presuppositions, deceived and duped an entire generation (from 1912 until the hoax was uncovered in 1953). Concerning this, John Reader said, "When preconception is so clearly defined, so easily reproduced, so enthusiastically welcomed and so long accommodated as in the case of the Piltdown man, science reveals a disturbing predisposition towards belief before investigation."[73]

What are the roots of evolutionary *faith*? The basis is anthropological. Molecular biologist Michael Denton said, "The entire scientific ethos and philosophy of modern western man is based to a large extent upon the central claim of Darwin's theory that humanity was not born by the creative intentions of a Deity, but by a completely mindless, trial and error selection of random molecular patterns."[74] An outstanding British biologist, D. M. S. Watson, said, "… the theory of evolution … a theory universally accepted, not because it can be proved by logically coherent evidence to be true, but because the only alternative—special creation—is clearly incredible."[75] According to Denton, Darwin's theory of evolution is "a highly speculative hypothesis entirely without direct factual support and very far from that self-evident axiom some of its more aggressive advocates would have us believe."[76] The building of modern evolutionary theory is founded, not upon evidence, but upon a paradigmical prejudice. To this, C. S. Lewis responded, "Was it devised not to get in facts but to keep out God?"[77] The evolutionary faith must be understood as *man's attempt to flee from God*. If God is Creator and is now sustaining every atom of His creation, then man is *faced with reminders of Him wherever he looks*. Rebellious man is suppressing the truth clearly seen in creation (Romans 1:18–20).

Since the roots of evolutionary faith are anthropological, then the touchstone of truth is man's reason. This culminates in the absolutization of the scientific method; that is, only what can be proved by man's reason is true. Revelation from a transcendent, Creator God is *not* a source of knowledge. But, by this very definition, evolution *cannot* be scientific! According to Denton:

> … the theory of evolution deals with a series of unique events, the origin of life, the origin of intelligence and so on. Unique events are unrepeatable and cannot be subjected to any sort of experimental investigation. Such events … may be the subject of much fascinating and controversial speculation, but their causation can, strictly speaking, never be subject to scientific validation. Furthermore, not only is the theory incapable of proof by normal scientific means, the evidence is … far from compelling.[78]

For the evolutionary faith, matter is ultimate. Dr. Corliss Lamont, one of the signers of *Humanist Manifesto II*, states that "… Nature itself constitutes the sum total of reality, that matter-energy and not mind is the foundation stuff of the universe … our cosmos does not possess a supernatural and eternal God."[79] Man is therefore only a product of the cosmos and is conditioned by it. Life is defined chemically and physiologically.

71.　　Ian T. Taylor, *In the Minds of Men* (Toronto: TFE Publishing, 1984), p. 194.

72.　　John Pfeiffer, "Man–Through Time's Mists," *The Saturday Evening Post*, 239th year, no. 25, 3 Dec. 1966, p. 41.

73.　　John Reader, *Missing Links* (London: Collins, 1981), p. 81.

74.　　Michael Denton. *Evolution: A Theory in Crisis* (Bethesda, MD: Adler & Adler, 1985), p. 357.

75.　　D. M. S. Watson, "Adaptation," *Nature*, 1929, 24:233.

76.　　Denton, p. 76.

77.　　C. S. Lewis, *They Asked for a Paper* (London: Geoffrey Bles, 1962), p. 163.

78.　　Denton, pp. 75–76.

79.　　Corliss Lamont, *The Philosophy of Humanism* (New York: Frederick Unger Publishing, 1977), pp. 12–13, 16.

Finally, for the evolutionary faith, the physical laws of the universe stand before us as impersonal absolutes.

What are the consequences of this faith? Quoting the *Humanist Manifesto II*, "Happiness and the creative realization of human needs and desires, individually and in shared enjoyment, are continuous themes of humanism. We strive for the good life, here and now."[80] Compare this the Apostle Paul's observation of those who reject the basic tenets of the Christian faith, "Let us eat and drink, for tomorrow we die" (I Corinthians 15:32).

According to Denton,

> The social and political currents [communism, fascism, socialism—J.N.] which have swept the world in the past eighty years would have been impossible without its [Darwinian Revolution—J.N.] intellectual sanction. It is ironic to recall, that it was the increasingly secular outlook in the nineteenth century which initially eased the way for the acceptance of evolution while today it is perhaps the Darwinian view of nature more than any other that is responsible for the agnostic and skeptical outlook of the twentieth century.[81]

Denton concludes his masterful treatise with these insightful comments:

> Ultimately the Darwinian theory of evolution is no more nor less that the great cosmogenic myth of the twentieth century.... [I]t satisfies the same deep psychological need for an all-embracing explanation of the origin of the world which has motivated all the cosmogenic myth makers of the past.[82]

C. S. Lewis shows us the heinous epistemological[83] ramifications that result from embracing this myth as truth:

> I grew up believing in this [Evolution] Myth and I have felt its almost perfect grandeur. Let no one say we are an unimaginative age; neither the Greeks nor the Norsemen ever invented a better story.... But the Myth asks me to believe that reason is simply the unforeseen and unintended by-product of a mindless process at one state of its endless and aimless becoming. The content of the Myth thus knocks from under me the only ground on which I could possibly believe the Myth to be true. If my own mind is a product of the irrational ... how shall I trust my mind when it tells me about Evolution?[84]

The Darwinian Revolution is nothing but a philosophy of despair. We are pieces of driftwood washed up on the shore of fate. Modern education has proclaimed this "evangel" for decades. The result is students who look at the stars and say, "Praise and honor to Big Bang, Chance, and Matter."

In contrast, what are the roots of biblical *faith*? The basis is theological. Biblical faith looks at what God has said in His revealed Word. The Bible reveals God to be the Creator, Triune, Sovereign, Just, Good, Infinite, Eternal, and Personal. The universe is His handiwork. Biblical faith admits man's rebellion and trusts in God's redemption in Christ. Biblical faith sees man to be accountable to his Creator. Man faces his Creator everywhere for no fact exists apart from God.

Since the roots of biblical faith are theological, then the touchstone of truth is revelation. True knowledge is founded upon the fear or respect of the biblical God; apart from this, we have, not knowledge, but misinformation (Proverbs 1:7; Psalm 36:9; Colossians 2:1–3). The purpose of the Bible is to correct our faulty, sin-corrupted vision so that we might see the world in truth.

For the biblical faith, God is ultimate. Man is responsible before Him to obey His directive to take dominion over the creation (Genesis 1:26–28; see also Psalm 8:6–8). James Clerk Maxwell (1831–1879) was a pioneering scientist in the field of electromagnetism. A prayer was found in his own handwriting after his death in which he quoted from this Genesis passage and indicated that

---

80.   Paul Kurtz, ed. *Humanist Manifestos I and II* (Amherst, NY: Prometheus Books, 1973), p. 17.
81.   Denton, p. 358.
82.   Denton, p. 358.
83.   The branch of philosophy that studies the nature of knowledge, its presuppositions and foundations, and its extent and validity.
84.   C. S. Lewis. *Christian Reflections*, ed. Walter Hooper (Grand Rapids: Eerdmans Publishing, 1975), p. 89.

God's command to man to subdue the earth was the motivation for his scientific studies.[85] He utilized his intense study of God's creation with one goal in mind—to benefit the inhabitants of Earth.

Finally, for the biblical faith, every physical "law of nature" is simply man's attempt to systematize the faithfulness of God in the performance of His omnipotent sustaining word of power (Hebrews 1:3). We may determine the "cause and effect" nature of the universe by observation, but we must always keep in mind that the *first cause* of these laws is the triune God.

What are the consequences of this faith? William Haller wrote, "Men who have assurance that they are to inherit heaven have a way of presently taking possession of the earth."[86] Physicist and theologian Stanley L. Jaki observed that "the history of science with its several stillbirths and only one viable birth, clearly shows that the only cosmology, or view of the cosmos as a whole, that was capable of generating science was a view of which the principal disseminator was the Gospel itself."[87] Biblical faith generated modern science. The scientific enterprise must now be subservient to biblical faith. Then, and only then, will its discoveries and products serve the "City of God" and thereby bring healing to the nations (Revelation 22:2).

Biblical faith will open our eyes to the awe and wonder of God's creation. We will amen the truth of the *Netherlands' Confession*, "Before our eyes as a beautiful book, in which all created things, large or small, are as letters showing the invisible things of God." We will echo the sentiments of the Psalmist, "Great are the works of the Lord; they are studied by all who delight in them" (Psalm 111:2).

Earth in Space by Design

Our Sun is positioned just perfectly in the Milky Way galaxy. If it would be nearer the galactic center, stronger cosmic radiation from the hub would make life impossible on Earth. Also, the stars in any constellation are at varying distances, some stars hundreds of times more distant than others. If our Solar System were located in another place in the Milky Way, the whole constellation scheme would be radically different. God placed our Solar System where it is so that the constellation arrangements would declare a unique story of His glory.

Concerning the arrangement of the Solar System, the distance of the Sun from Earth and the mass and size of the Sun is just right to support life on Earth and no other planet. The planetary system is so finely tuned that if the mass of Jupiter were to be increased by *1 percent*, the planetary system would no longer have that stability that is the precondition of life on Earth.

On any other planet, we would have been barred, or at least greatly impeded, from acquiring knowledge about the Solar System. The Moon and Sun have the same apparent size as viewed from Earth. This is because the diameter of the Sun is four hundred times the diameter of the Moon and its distance from Earth is four hundred times that of the Moon. This precise arrangement makes possible total eclipses, a phenomenon crucial to the development of astronomy. It made possible those attainments that are the basis of Ptolemaic or geocentric (Earth is the center of the Solar System) astronomy. Without Ptolemy's astronomy there would be no Copernican astronomy and Newtonian physics. On any other planet, Newton would have no Moon to verify the universality of the law of gravitation. You cannot see the Moons of Mars from its surface. The Moons of Jupiter and Saturn would appear much bigger than our Moon. Our Sun would look like a very bright star, not that imposing though not overpowering fiery body that could prompt a Copernican belief in heliocentricity (Sun is the center of the Solar System). Without this unique positioning, Newtonian physics would not have developed, let alone modern physics.

---

85.   Henry Morris. *Men of Science, Men of God* (San Diego: Master Book Publications, 1984), p. 91.

86.   William Haller. *The Rise of Puritanism*, p. 162. Cited in Gary North, ed. "Symposium on Puritanism and Progress," *The Journal of Christian Reconstruction*, VI:1, (Vallecito, CA: Chalcedon, 1979), p. 27.

87.   Stanley L. Jaki, *The Origin of Science and the Science of its Origins* (Edinburgh: Scottish Academic Press, 1978), p. 99.

The inclination of the axis of Earth is exactly 23.5°. The axis points north toward a star (within historically recorded times) bright enough to make possible the observation of the precession of Earth's axis (see Appendix Eleven). This occurred before the invention of the telescope, a pivotal feat in astronomy. No such star reference point exists in the Southern Hemisphere. Without this tilt, the four seasons would be nonexistent. Without the four seasons, it would be impossible to grow food on large portions of the world. The four seasons reveal the covenant faithfulness of our God, the Creator and Sustainer of all things:

> While the earth remains, seedtime and harvest, cold and heat, winter and summer, and day and night shall not cease (Genesis 8:22).

Our Earth is an amazing planet. Its crust and its composition are just right to support life. The quantity and composition of the ocean are just right to support life. Water is essential to life. The world has 4.1×10^{16} cubic feet of water. There is not one drop of water anywhere else in our Solar System! The composition of the atmosphere is just right to support life. 21% of our atmosphere is made up of life-giving oxygen (O_2). No other satellite or planet in our Solar System has free oxygen like this. The poisonous ozone (O_3) layer surrounds Earth at a safe distance of ten miles above the surface. It absorbs and filters out deadly ultraviolet light from the Sun.

Truly, God has carefully positioned Earth in space. This placement provides life for its inhabitants. Its position was also perfect for developing astronomy, a most crucial component in developing science as a tool to take dominion over God's creation.

More North Circumpolar Constellations

Cassiopeia

Cassiopeia makes a conspicuous "W" or "M" in the northern sky. In Arabic, it is El Seder meaning "the freed." The Egyptians called this constellation Set, meaning "set up as queen." In the Chaldee tongue, it was known as Dat al Cursa meaning "enthroned." Three stars of Cassiopeia are Schedir (magnitude 2.23 at 147 light-years) meaning "the freed," Ruchbah (magnitude 2.68 at 43 light-years) meaning "the enthroned or the seated," and Caph (magnitude 2.25 at 45 light-years) meaning "the branch."

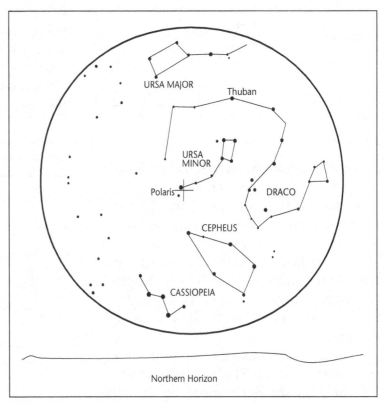

Figure 2–10: North Circumpolar Stars

In 1572, a great supernova[88] (called Tycho's star) burst forth in this constellation. On November 11 of that year, the famous astronomer Tycho Brahe[89] (1546–1601) made these comments:

> On the eleventh day of November in the evening after sunset ... I was contemplating the stars in a clear sky ... I noticed that a new and unusual star, surpassing the other stars in brilliancy,

---

88.   A rare celestial phenomenon involving the explosion of most of the material in a star, resulting in an extremely bright, short-lived object that emits vast amounts of energy.

89.   Pronounced *tee-ko bra-hee.*

was shining almost directly above my head; and since I had, from boyhood, known all the stars of the heavens perfectly, it was quite evident to me that there had never been any star in that place in the sky, even the smallest, to say nothing of a star so conspicuous and bright as this. I was so astonished at this sight that I was not ashamed to doubt the trustworthiness of my own eyes. But when I observed that others, on having the place pointed out to them, could see that there was really a star there, I had no further doubts. A miracle indeed, one that has never been previously seen before out time, in any age since the beginning of the world.[90]

Figure 2–11: Cassiopeia

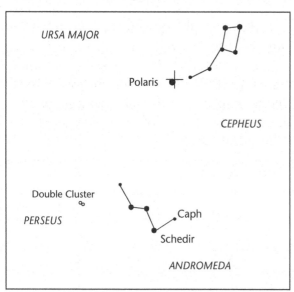

For a period of two weeks, this celestial explosion outshone every star in the sky. You could even see it in the daytime. It began to fade at the end of November and finally vanished from naked-eye sight in March of 1574. It created a great commotion in its time and induced the Protestant Reformer Theodore Beza (1519–1605) to predict the Second Coming of Christ. Some even considered it as a re-appearance of the "Star of Bethlehem."

A beautiful celestial grouping called the Double Cluster lies between Cassiopeia and Perseus. On a really dark night, you can see this patch of light with the naked eye. A small telescope or binoculars will reveal that this cloudy spot consists of two open star clusters, both about 7,000 light-years distant. According to some astronomers, this pair forms one of the most impressive and spectacular objects in the night sky.

Draco

In the Greek, Draco means "trodden on." Draco is possibly derived from the Hebrew, Dahrach, meaning "to tread." The Egyptians named this constellation Herfent, meaning "the serpent accursed." The Hebrews called it Rastaban, meaning "the head of the subtle who is to be destroyed." Hercules, a mighty warrior, is pictured as treading under foot the head of Draco, the dragon.

The most famous and brightest star of this constellation is Thuban (magnitude 3.64 at 220 light-years) meaning "the subtle." As already mentioned, about 4,000 years ago, Thuban was the "North (or Pole) Star" and worshipped as such by the ancient Egyptians. Much has been written

Figure 2–12: Draco

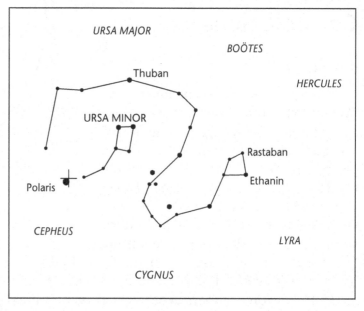

about this star and its connection to the Great Pyramid of Khufu at Gizeh, the most mathematically perfect and puzzling structure in the world. In summary, it appears as though one of its descending passageways was constructed to point directly at Thuban as this star passed its lower culmination[91]

90.   Cited in Robert Burnham Jr., vol. 1, p. 505.
91.   *Lower culmination* is the lowest point in the sky that Thuban reaches as it makes its circular path around the North Pole.

point below the North Pole. In 1929, Charles Barns, author of *1001 Celestial Wonders*, described his reaction during a visit to this wonder of the world:

> I myself, some years ago, crept down into the sepulchral chambers deep in the solid masonry of this most ancient of tomb observatories, and gazing obliquely up through the murky rift, beheld a rectangular patch of blue Egyptian sky where Thuban once reigned in solemn grandeur—a thrilling moment![92]

Cepheus

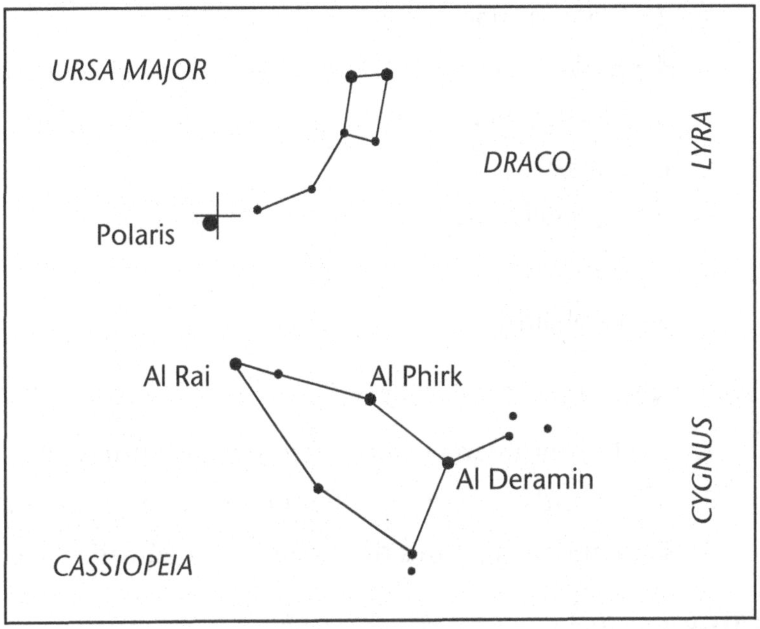

In Egypt, this constellation was known as Pe-ku-hor, meaning "this one cometh to rule." In Greek, Cepheus means "the branch." Individual stars of this constellation are Al Deramin (magnitude of 2.44 at 52 light-years) meaning "coming quickly," Al Phirk (magnitude of 3.15 at 980 light-years) meaning "the redeemer," and Al Rai (magnitude of 3.20 at 51 light-years) meaning "who bruises or breaks."

Delta Cephei is a famous variable star. It pulsates (i.e., changes magnitude) not because it is eclipsed by a companion star, but because of internal energy change that affects its surface temperature—hence also its spectral type. There are many other

Figure 2–13: Cepheus

stars (approximately 500) that do this and they are called Cepheids in honor of this star. Astronomer John Goodricke first noticed this characteristic of Delta Cephei in 1784. The magnitude of Delta Cephei varies from a low of 3.51 to a high of 4.42 every 5.37 days. Delta is a supergiant star that is thirty times the size of our Sun. Astronomers use the periodicity of a Cepheid to determine its distance from Earth (see Appendix Twelve). Delta Cephei is 1,300 light-years away.

What is the message of these stars?

What can we learn from the ancient meanings of the star names of these North Circumpolar Stars? The meanings for the stars of Ursa Major and Ursa Minor suggest that these constellations symbolize the shelter and protection afforded to a flock of sheep. Cassiopeia speaks of a woman raised up as a queen after being released from bondage. Draco speaks of a cursed serpent being bruised or trodden on. In fact, the feet of Hercules, a victorious warrior (see Chapter Five), is crushing the head of Draco, the serpent. Cepheus speaks of a redeemer who comes quickly to bruise or to break an enemy.

Any astute Bible student can readily associate these signs with the Gospel of Christ. Christ is that victorious warrior, the redeemer of His people, His sheep, His bride (or queen). He released His people from the bondage of sin by crushing the head of the serpent, the Devil, on Calvary's Cross (Genesis 3:15). After redeeming His people, God set His bride on His throne (Ephesians 2:6) and protects and guards them as their Great Shepherd who has risen from the dead (Hebrews 13:20; I Peter 1:5).

---

92.   Cited in Robert Burnham Jr., vol. 2, pp. 862–863.

Questions for Review and Further Study

Short sentence answers:

Define the following words:

1. Circumpolar stars
2. Magnitude
3. Constellation
4. Binary star
5. North Celestial Pole
6. Galaxy
7. Ozone layer
8. Supernova
9. Cepheids

Short essay:

1. Explain how Greek letters relate to star names.
2. Study and explain the difference between apparent and absolute magnitude.
3. Describe the pictures that are associated with the constellations Ursa Major and Ursa Minor.

Long essay:

1. Explain God's providence in association with Polaris.
2. Define the size and structure of the Milky Way.
3. How would you respond to the following statement?

   "The chance, impersonal forces of evolution put Earth where it is now in space."

Research:

1. Research and report on the different types (called classes) of galaxies.

2. Do a research project on the science of spectroscopy.

Figure 2–14: Simple Spectrograph

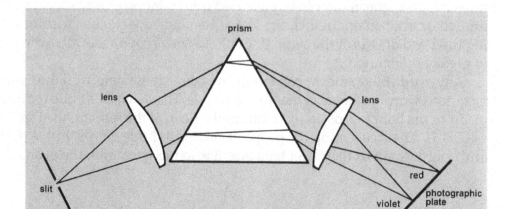

Chapter Three
Star Movements During The Night

As indicated earlier in the discussion of the Big Dipper Clock, the stars appear to move during the night. According to the heliocentric theory, the rotation of Earth causes this movement of the stars. The stars are so far away that their individual movements cannot be detected except by special techniques.

Geocentricity or Heliocentricity?

According to the geocentric or Ptolemaic view, Earth is at rest[93] and the universe, including our Sun and all the stars, travel around it daily. According to the heliocentric view, this is the apparent situation, but it does not reflect the way things really are. Like the motion of our Sun, the stars just "appear" to move in arcs in the sky, from east to west. Someone once told the philosopher Ludwig Wit-

Figure 3–1: Star Movements

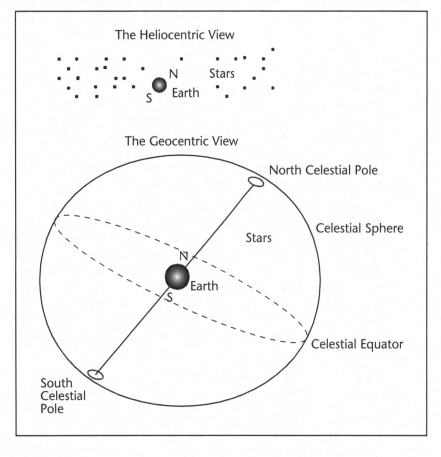

The Heliocentric View

N
S Earth   Stars

The Geocentric View

North Celestial Pole

Celestial Sphere

Stars

N
Earth
S

Celestial Equator

South Celestial Pole

---

93.   Or stationary. Geostationism is a synonym for geocentricism.

tgenstein (1889–1951) how stupid and superstitious medieval Europeans were before the time of Copernicus to have looked at the sky and thought the Sun was circling Earth.[94] He is said to have replied, "I agree. But I wonder what it would have looked like if the sun had been circling the earth."[95] *It would have looked exactly the same!* Medieval people had nothing but their naked eye as an astronomical tool. We, if living in the same era, would have also embraced geocentricity.

This commitment to geocentricism is one of many reasons why our culture today tends to look back on its European ancestors with disdain and disgust. Underlying this disdain is an antagonism to the Christian faith that the medieval Europeans confessed. This presuppositional antithesis must be understood whenever the heliocentric/geocentric issue is discussed. To illustrate this, read the chapter entitled "In the Light of the Above" in *The Day the Universe Changed* by scientific writer James Burke (1936–). Then read the chapter entitled "The Social Conditions for Wealth" in *Making Sense of Your Dollars*[96] by economist Ian Hodge. This reading assignment will exhibit how one's presuppositions affect one's understanding and retelling of history. Also note these pertinent observations from medieval scholar William Carrol Bark:

> … the early medieval society was a pioneer society living on a frontier, both geographical and intellectual, and engaged in advancing it. It is remarkable that historians of the West should so long have failed to apprehend this absolutely vital truth about the origins of their own tradition…. To say that the medieval Church occupied a leading position, in part because of the social backwardness of the time, is not to say that its influence was always and everywhere overwhelming and that there were no motives, interests, or activities except those inspired by religion; then, as in other times, men, even churchmen, were not always true to their principles, and the Church did not always win out in its struggles with secular forces. What is important … is that the Church was powerful enough to win most of its battles and to play a part in many events that were not, strictly speaking, its concern; and above all, that in the fourth and fifth centuries, when the classical spirit was almost dead in the West, along with the Roman form of political administration and much of the rest of the old social system, the Christian spirit that was to create a new civilization was full of life and hope and confidence.[97]

> … yet to Western man since the Renaissance, the historian as well as the philosopher, the artist, and the scientist, it has been all but unpalatable. Blinded by our prejudice in favor of classical 'civilization' as contrasted with medieval 'barbarism,' we have grossly misinterpreted the creative character of what was taking place in late Roman and early medieval times. We have confused adjustment with decay, and failing to recognize what may be called a change of pace and direction, we have branded it as exclusively an ending…. What may seem today to have been quite simply retrogression and nothing else, may from another point of view be regarded as a cutting away of dead wood.[98]

> … something new, distinct, and essentially original began in the Western European portion of the Roman Empire … best described as a new attitude toward life…. Perhaps the worst menace of all has been certain powerful *idées fixes*: the preoccupation with the vast epic of the decline and fall; the 'authoritative' conviction that the early Middle Ages were a time of superstitious ignorance and general lethargy, enlivened only by fitful flashes of barbaric violence and cruelty. The imperceptive but unforgettable image of 'vultures feeding on the carrion' and 'maggots crawling in the carcass,' conjured up by Toynbee, may be mentioned in passing…. We know now that the Dark Age was not that dark. Ignorance, lethargy, and disorder existed then as now, but they were far from blighting an age eager for learning, vigor-

---

94. The *Almagest*, written by the Alexandrian (i.e., Greek) mathematician and astronomer Ptolemy popularized geocentricity for the masses. Ptolemy summarized the theories of most of the ancient Greek scientists. There was one Greek scientist who disagreed with geocentricity. His name was Aristarchus of Samos (ca. 310–230 B.C.) and he was the first to put forward the heliocentric hypothesis. See Sir Thomas Heath, *Aristarchus of Samos: The Ancient Copernicus* (New York: Dover Publications, [1913] 1981).
95. Cited in James Burke, *The Day the Universe Changed* (Boston: Little, Brown and Company, 1985), p. 11.
96. Published by Ross House Books, 1995.
97. William Carrol Bark, *Origins of the Medieval World* (Stanford: Stanford University Press, 1958). pp. 28–29.
98. Bark, p. 65.

ous in living and in expressing itself, and idealistically constructive. Perhaps it is not too much to say that medieval society was functional in ways not even dreamed of by antiquity and leading to ends beyond the imagination of earlier times. By 'functional' I mean that it was a working, striving society, impelled to pioneer, forced to experiment, often making mistakes but also drawing upon the energies of its people much more fully than its predecessors, and eventually allowing them much fuller and freer scope for development. That conditions, events, and peoples came together as they did in the early Middle Ages was extremely fortunate for the present heirs of the Western tradition…. The element of freedom stands out, or more accurately, the *preparation* for eventual freedom and individualism and dignity. The deeds and events of the period served a pathfinding function…. One of those goals, perhaps the most important of all, was freedom—for we can now see and recognize what our predecessors could not discern. Certain fundamental adjustments had to be made before truly significant advances could be made in technology; the West had first to be free from the domination of rigid social institutions obstructive of new methods, free to invent, experiment, borrow, and apply. We have seen how those alterations began to come about in the intellectual sphere, in the changed relation between State and individual, in the honorable position accorded labor through the powerful monastic institution and the missionary activity of the monks, in the status of women through the teachings of Christianity. There was in simple truth a renovation literally from the ground up in the rural, agrarian society of medieval Europe. True, the rights of women, serfs, slaves, individuals in general, long remained theoretical rather than actual, just as, for example, in the feudal system the rights of the king long existed more in theory than in fact…. From the monks and scholastic philosophers, so long despised as dolts, denied the favor of detached, 'scientific' examination, and hence unappreciated, were to come theories and applications which in time would enable Western man further to emancipate himself by winning domination over his physical environment. One of the first of many steps toward freedom from drudgery, for example, came with the development of the horse-drawn heavy plow; the full contributory effect of the scholastic revolution that began with the early theological controversies of the Patristic Age and continued throughout the Middle Ages is only in the process of being investigated.[99]

Our modern textbooks also put a presuppositional spin on the heliocentric views propagated by Nicholaus Copernicus (1473–1543). This spin is that when Copernicus disengaged himself from the Ptolemaic view by hypothesizing that a rotating Earth circles the Sun, he dethroned man from a place of significance in the universe. Modern writers have made much of the lofty place of man in the view of medieval culture. Note Arthur O. Lovejoy's analysis:

> It has often been said that the older picture of the world in space was peculiarly fitted to give man a high sense of his own importance and dignity; and some modern writers have made much of this supposed implication of pre-Copernican astronomy. Man occupied, we are told, the central place in the universe, and round the planet of his habitation all the vast, unpeopled spheres obsequiously revolved. But the actual tendency of the geocentric system was, for the medieval mind, precisely the opposite. For the centre of the world was not a position of honor; it was rather the place farthest removed from the Empyrean [See footnote 27.], the bottom of the creation, to which its dregs and baser elements sank. The actual centre, indeed, was Hell; in the spatial sense the medieval world was literally diabolocentric [devil-centered]. And the whole sublunary region was, of course, incomparably inferior to the resplendent and incorruptible heavens above the moon…. It is sufficiently evident from such passages that the geocentric cosmography served rather for man's humiliation than for his exaltation, and that Copernicanism was opposed partly on the ground that it assigned too dignified and lofty a position to his dwelling-place.[100]

It was for the promotion of man's exaltation that the Renaissance humanists advocated Copernican cosmology. By enthroning man, humanism of that time and this time dethrones God from His place of loftiness and power.

---

99. Bark, pp. 99–100.
100. Arthur O. Lovejoy, *The Great Chain of Being: A Study of the History of an Idea* (New York: Harper Torchbook, [1936] 1965), pp. 101–102.

Copernicus adopted heliocentricity because of its simplicity. To him, the Ptolemaic theory, founded upon epicycles,[101] although accurate in terms of celestial measurements of the time, was too complicated. Later, Johannes Kepler (1571–1630) refined the theory with the elliptical motions of the planets, although his mentor, Tycho Brahe (1546–1601), clung to a revised version of geocentricity.[102]

Geocentricity as a valid scientific theory is considered today to be a dead issue.[103] This is so for two basic reasons. First, with the coming of more accurate instrumentation, scientists have been able to measure stellar parallax (see Appendix Seven). Second, with the launching of the Russian *Sputnik* on October 4, 1957, geosynchronous satellites present a physical situation that geocentricity cannot account for. Geosynchronous satellites travel above Earth's equator from west to east at an altitude of approximately 22,300 miles and at a speed matching that of Earth's rotation. Thus they remain stationary in the sky in relationship to Earth. It is because they "appear" to be stationary that *we know that they are moving*. They remain in this orbit because their centrifugal motion away from Earth is counterbalanced by the gravitational pull of Earth. If, as the geocentric theory states, Earth is stationary, then these satellites do not move. If these satellites do not move, then there is no physical force pushing them away from Earth to counterbalance the pull of Earth's gravity. If this is so, these satellites should not stay up there at 22,300 miles; *they should fall down*. To account for these satellites staying up in the sky violating the law of gravity, the geocentric scientist must present a valid and testable physical theory. This accounting has not yet been done.[104]

The Celestial Sphere

The geocentric theory is very convenient for observational astronomy. We can assume that all the stars are attached to a huge, imaginary sphere called the Celestial Sphere. Many ancient scientists believed that the stars hung like lamps from this spherical dome in the sky. Modern scientists use this idea as a tool to help them plot the position of the stars in the sky. Every star occupies a unique position on the Celestial Sphere. Scientists have developed a coordinate system similar to the latitude-longitude system of Earth. On this coordinate system, we find, as already mentioned, a North Celestial Pole, a South Celestial Pole, and a Celestial Equator. These locations are mere extensions of Earth's North Pole, South Pole, and equator onto the Celestial Sphere. Stars are located on the Celestial Sphere using *right ascension* (R.A. or α, the Greek letter alpha) in hours and *declination* (Dec. or δ, the Greek letter delta) in degrees. Right ascension in hours is similar to longitude except that R.A. varies from zero hours to twenty-three hours. Each hour represents 15°. Declination is similar to latitude. Stars north of the Celestial Equator are identified in the range between 0° and +90°. Stars south of the Celestial Equator are identified in the range between 0° and -90°.

---

101. An epicycle is a small circle, the center of which moves on the circumference of a larger circle at whose center is Earth and the circumference of which describes the orbit of one of the planets around Earth.

102. At that time, the five known planets were supposed to revolve around the Sun, which, with the planets, circled Earth each year.

103. A small group of scientists still hold strongly to the position, however. See Gerardus D. Bouw, *Geocentricity* (Association for Biblical Astronomy [Tychonian Society], 1992 [1984]) and Walter van der Kamp, *The Cosmos, Einstein and Truth* (self-published by the author who lives in Victoria, British Columbia, 1993). For more information on geocentricity as a model of the universe, write to: Association for Biblical Astronomy, 4527 Wetzel Avenue, Cleveland, OH 44109 USA.

104. In spite of this problem, geocentrists claim the Bible to support their view. For example, did not the Sun "stand still" (Joshua 10:12–13) in Joshua's day? If the Bible teaches heliocentricity, then, according to geocentrists, Joshua should have said, "Earth, stop rotating!" The Hebrew word for "stood" means "to be dumbfounded, to be astonished, to hold its peace, to be quiet, to be silent." Yes, the Sun did not appear to move in the sky, but was it literally dumbfounded, astonished, holding to its peace, quiet and silent? At this point, we need some sound principles of biblical hermeneutics (science of interpretation). For a constructive analysis, see James B. Jordan, "The Geocentricity Question," in *The Biblical Educator* 3 (1981):12.

Looking to the north, the stars travel in a counterclockwise direction. Looking to the south, the stars travel in a clockwise direction.

Earth rotates 360° (one revolution) in less than 24 hours; to be exact, 23 hours, 56 minutes, and 4.09 seconds. This is called a sidereal[105] day. A solar day is 24 hours. The difference between 24 hours and the period of one revolution is:

$$
\begin{array}{ll}
24 \text{ hours} & \\
\underline{-23 \text{ hours,} \quad 56 \text{ minutes,} \quad 4.09 \text{ seconds}} & \\
\phantom{-23 \text{ hours,}} \quad 3 \text{ minutes,} \quad 55.91 \text{ seconds} &
\end{array}
$$

A solar day is the time it takes for Earth to rotate 360° plus 3.0 minutes, 55.91 seconds. In other words, in 24 hours Earth rotates 360.986°.

Each star, therefore, makes a complete revolution of 360° on the Celestial Sphere in a sidereal, not solar day. This means that each star makes slightly more than one revolution (360.986°) in a 24-hour period. After a star completes one revolution, it begins the next revolution in the remaining three minutes and fifty-six seconds. It is easy to verify this by observation. A star that appears on the horizon, say, at 9 P.M. on a Monday evening will be slightly above the horizon at 9 P.M. on the following evening. Wednesday evening at 9 P.M., the star will be still further above

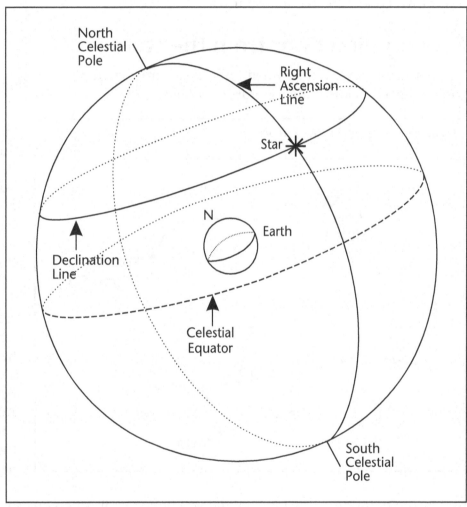

Figure 3–2: The Celestial Sphere

the horizon. A month later, at 9 P.M., the star will be considerably above the horizon. After three months, at 9 P.M., the star will be a quarter of a circle away from the eastern horizon. At the end of a year, the star will have completed an apparent circle. This means that, every month of the year, the stars pass through the same places in the sky. What a wonderful timepiece God has made in the night sky! According to heliocentricity, the real movement is, not of the stars, but of the spin of Earth and its rotation about the Sun. Earth completes one revolution around the Sun in twelve months.

---

105. From the Latin *sidereus* meaning "constellation or star."

With a little more mathematics, we can discover how many degrees a star will travel in one hour. Since the stars travel 360° every 1,436.0682 minutes (23 hours, 56 minutes, 4.09 seconds), then, in four minutes they will travel:

$$(360)(4/1436.0682) = 1.003° \text{ or } 1°$$

Therefore, in one hour, a star travels 15° (60°/4). A convenient measuring tool for measuring the night sky is the handspan. If you hold the fingers and thumb apart at the end of your outstretched arm, the degree measure from your thumb to your little finger measures approximately 20°.[106] Hence, in one hour, a star travels close to one handspan.

Finding directions from the stars

There may come a time when, in some emergency at night, you may need to know the compass directions.

Figure 3–3: Hand Measures

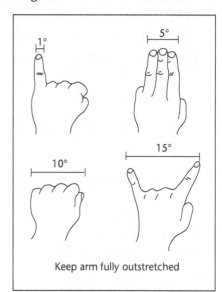

Keep arm fully outstretched

Find Polaris, the North Star, which is almost exactly due north (off by 1°). You can find this star by using the pointers (Dubhe and Merak) of the Big Dipper (Ursa Major). Extend the distance between Merak and Dubhe six times beyond Dubhe and you will find Polaris.

In the Southern Hemisphere, there are two ways in which the Southern Cross will help you find due south.

First, point one arm to Beta Centauri and the other to Achernar (Alpha Eridanus). Bring both arms together and they will be aimed at a point near the South Celestial Pole. Lower the arms vertically until they are pointing to the horizon and you have the direction due south.

Figure 3–4: Big and Little Dippers

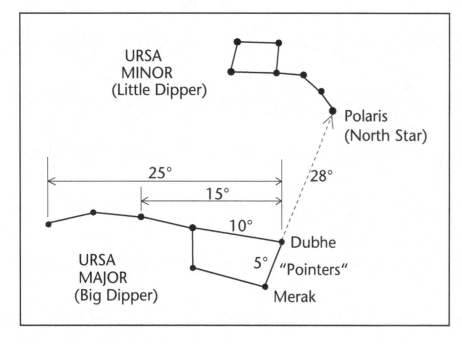

Second, visually extend the long axis of the Southern Cross about 4 times its length beyond Alpha Crucis (the star on the base on the cross). This will roughly give the position of the South Celestial Pole. Again, a point on the horizon vertically below the South Celestial Pole gives the direction of due south.

---

106. Everybody has a standard angular measuring device—the outstretched arm. Although everyone has different-sized hands, the proportion of the length of your arms to the width of your hands is nearly the same for all people.

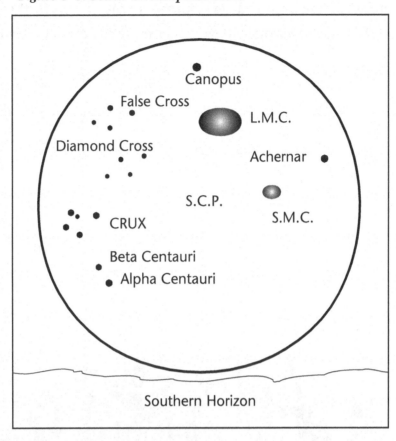

Figure 3–5: South Circumpolar Stars

Questions for Review and Further Study

Short sentence answers:

1. Define the following words:
   a. Celestial Sphere
   b. Celestial Equator
   c. Right ascension
   d. Declination
   e. Handspan

2. Which direction (counterclockwise or clockwise) do the stars travel when you look south? north?

Short essay:

1. Using correct astronomical terminology, explain how you locate stars on the "Celestial Sphere."
2. A star travels how many degrees in one hour? How is this figure derived?
3. Explain how to find the direction "due north" by looking at the North Circumpolar Stars.
4. Explain how to find the direction "due south" by looking at the South Circumpolar Stars.

Research:

1. Do a research project on the historical development of the geocentric theory of the heavens.

2. Do a research project on the historical development of the heliocentric theory of the heavens.

Chapter Four
Seasonal Stars

You can see the North Circumpolar Stars throughout the year. Now, we are going to survey the seasonal stars. You see these stars by facing south. As we look to the left, these stars will be rising in the east and eventually moving across the sky to our right, finally setting in the west. In this chapter, we will take a brief journey through the four seasons, starting with winter, detailing the brightest stars with their attendant constellations. As in Chapter Two, we will discuss the scientific characteristics of these stars, some associated deep sky wonders, some lore associated with them, and define the meaning of their names.

The Winter Stars

There are six major constellations that brighten the winter skies: Orion, Canis Major, Canis Minor, Taurus, Gemini, and Auriga. The stars of Orion begin to rise in the east at 9 P.M. in late October. All six constellations are clearly seen at 9 P.M. during the months of January, February, and March.

Figure 4–1: Big Dipper in Winter

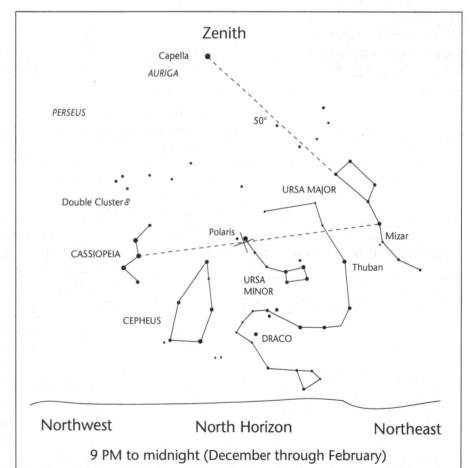

9 PM to midnight (December through February)

Orion

Orion, nicknamed the hunter, is a spectacular constellation, replete with intricate marvels. The ancient Egyptians named this constellation Hagat, meaning "he who triumphs." The ancient Akkadians named it Urana, "the light of heaven." The Hebrews called it Oarian, meaning "light." A very popular Arabian name for Orion was Al Babdur meaning "The Strong One"; better known is the Arabian name Al Jabbar, "The Giant." The American poet Henry Wadsworth Longfellow's (1807–1882) *Occultation of Orion* builds on these ancient Arabic names:

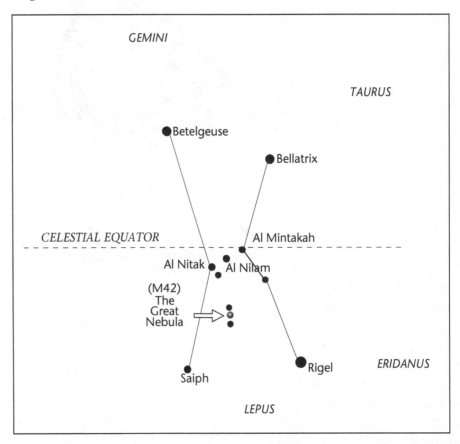

Figure 4–2: Orion

> Begirt with many a blazing star,
> Stood the great giant Algebar,
> Orion, hunter of the beast!
> His sword hung gleaming by his side,
> And on his arm, the lion's hide
> Scattered across the midnight air
> The golden radiance of its hair....

British poet Alfred, Lord Tennyson's (1809–1892) *Locksley Hall* is equally well known for its allusion to this glittering constellation:

> Many a night from yonder ivied
> casement, ere I went to rest,
> Did I look on great Orion, sloping
> slowly to the west.

Orion's "belt and sword" asterim[107] serves as a good direction finder. One of its stars, Delta Orionis (Al Mintakah) is almost exactly on the Celestial Equator, the projection of Earth's equator on the Celestial Sphere. The Celestial Equator meets our horizon due east and due west. When Orion's

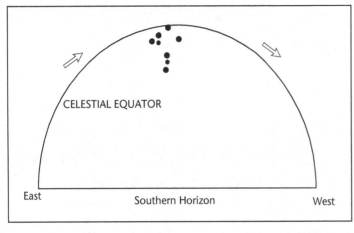

Figure 4–3: "Belt and Sword" Direction Finder

"belt and sword" rise above the horizon, therefore, you are looking due east. When it sets, you are

---

107.   Stargazers in the Southern Hemisphere call this asterim the "saucepan."

looking due west. When the sword is straight down (at its zenith[108]), you are looking due south. You can judge the other directions by estimating the angle at which the "belt and sword" are tilted.

The Bible refers to this constellation three times:

> Who makes the Bear, Orion, and the Pleiades, and the chambers of the south (Job 9:9).

> He who made the Pleiades and Orion … The Lord is His name (Amos 5:8).

> Can you bind the chains of the Pleiades, or loose the cords of Orion (Job 38:31)?

Betelgeuse, Alpha Orionis, is the eleventh brightest star in the sky. With a golden orange or deep topaz color, this supergiant (3000°K) is estimated to be between 550 and 920 times the size of our Sun. *It is the single largest created thing that the naked eye can see.* Picture it as a sphere big enough to enclose a twenty-story building. In comparison, the size of Earth would be the size of the period at the end of this sentence. Imagine this sphere as an empty jar and that we can unscrew its lid and pour in balls the size of Earth at the rate of 100/second. It would take 30,000 years to fill the jar. It would, in the place of our Sun, fill our Solar System, at minimum, to the orbit of Mars and, at maximum, to the orbit of Jupiter. It is so big that it appears as a disk, not a point of light, when viewed through the Hubble Space telescope. Its average diameter is 700,000,000 miles.

It is a variable star. Its brightness varies from a minimum magnitude of 1.2 to a maximum magnitude of -0.4. It flickers bright (6th brightest star shining with the light of 14,000 Suns), then dim (11th brightest star shining with the light of 7,600 Suns), in a 14 month period. Its average magnitude is 0.7. Its distance is 520 light-years.

Betelgeuse means "the right hand" (actually "house of two or twins" in Arabic) or, more anciently, "the coming of the branch." Scripture often calls the Lord Jesus a "branch," especially in the Old Testament prophets (see Jeremiah 23:5 and Isaiah 11:1–5).

Rigel, Beta Orionis, is the seventh brightest star in the sky with a magnitude of 0.14. Bluish-white in color and blazing hot (12,000°K), it is fifty times as wide as our Sun and 57,000 times as bright (making it one of the most luminous objects known in our galaxy). If its distance was 36 light-years (like Arcturus, Alpha Boötes), our nightly landscape would tingle with Rigel shadows and the night sky would always reflect the brightness of the Full Moon. Most of the starry sky would disappear from view! It is 900 light-years away—so remote, that it sits on the next spiral arm of the Milky Way.

Rigel means "leg" (actually "foot" in Arabic), or, more anciently, "the foot that crushes." In Scripture, the foot of Jesus crushed Satan on the Cross of Calvary (Genesis 3:15).

Figure 4–4: Horsehead Nebula

Bellatrix, Gamma Orionis, is a bluish-white star with a magnitude of 1.64 and is 470 light-years away. It means "quickly coming to swiftly destroy." Saiph, Kappa Orionis, means "bruised." It has a magnitude of 2.06 and is 2,100 light-years away.

Three stars form the "belt" of Orion. God asked Job if he could "loose" the cords of this belt. The three stars are, from left to right, Al Nitak (Zeta Orionis), Al Nilam (Epsilon Orionis), and Al Mintakah (Delta Orionis). Tennyson, called the poet of science, spoke of this triad as "those three stars of the airy Giant's zone that glitter burnished by the frosty dark." All three are about 1,600 light-years away and they are "loosed" in the sense that they are not bound to each other by any gravitational forces.

Bluish-white Al Nitak means "the girdle" or, more anciently, "the wounded one." It is a triple star and lies in a remarkable field of bright nebulosity. Just below it lies the famous Horsehead Nebula. The shape of this gas/dust

---

108. The highest point above the observer's horizon attained by a celestial body. The point opposite the zenith on the Celestial Sphere is called the *nadir*.

cloud resembles the head of a horse. To the left of Al Nitak lies NGC 2024, a glowing cloud consisting of bright and dark areas in a vast complexity of interior minutiae. Al Nilam has a magnitude of 1.7 and is also bluish-white in color. Al Mintakah is the same color and has a magnitude of 2.2.

In the sword lies Iota (Na'ir al Saiph), the "brightly bruised." About one-half degree to the north lies the Great Orion Nebula (M42 or NGC 1976). It is a mass of greenish haze visible to the naked eye. In a telescope, it appears to be a vast, swirling cloud of gas. NGC 1977, a smaller nebulosity, lies directly above it. In the heart of M42, lies Theta Orionis, part of a beautiful binary star system. Amid the soft glow of the surrounding gas, these stars seem to glisten and sparkle. Concerning M42, astronomers call it "the most remarkable, delicate, intricate, and beautiful nebula in the heavens." Again, let Tennyson's *Merlin and Vivien* enthrall you with its descriptive phrases of M42:

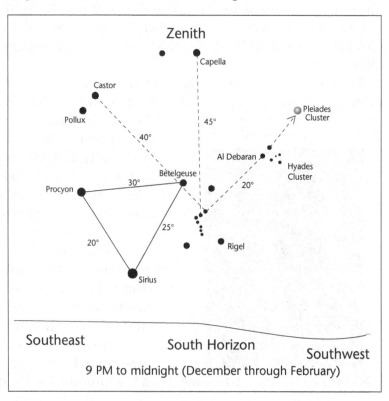

Figure 4–5: M42

> *… regions of lucid matter taking form,*
> *Brushes of fire, hazy gleams,*
> *Clusters and beds of worlds, and bee-like swarms*
> *Of Suns and starry streams …*

The Orion Nebula is truly one of the most awe-inspiring sights that the eye can behold. In this context, biblical Christians echo the Psalmist David,

> When I consider Your heavens, the work of Your fingers, the moon and the stars, which You have ordained, What is man that You are mindful of him, and the son of man that You visit him? For you have made him a little lower than the angels, and You have crowned him with glory and honor. (Psalm 8:3–5).

Based upon the star-name meanings, this constellation seems to point to the person and work of Christ. As a branch, He came to destroy the work of the enemy by receiving deadly wounds on Calvary's Cross.

The Great Winter Triangle

The three stars that form a distinct triangle in the sky are Betelgeuse, Sirius, and Procyon. The latter two are members of Canis Major and Canis Minor respectively.

Sirius, the brightest star in the sky (magnitude of -1.42), is "just" 8.7 light-years away. In terms of light-years, its distance is short, but, from another perspective, it is 550,000 times more distant than our Sun! If our galaxy were the size of the continental United States, it would sit about 500 yards away.

Its rising in the east (9 P.M. in mid December) reveals a twinkling kaleidoscope of rapidly changing color (due to the refraction of its light through the prism-like layers of air in our atmosphere). As it gains in elevation, all of its light reaches our eyes simultaneously and produces its distinct bluish-whiteness signifying that it is a very hot star; in fact, twice as hot as our Sun. In the words of Martha E. Martin,

> He comes rich in many colors, twinkling fast and changing with each motion from tints of ruby to sapphire and emerald and amethyst. As he rises higher and higher in the sky he gains composure and his beams now sparkle like the most brilliant diamond—not a pure white, but slightly tinged with iridescence.[109]

Figure 4–7: Canis Major/Minor and Gemini

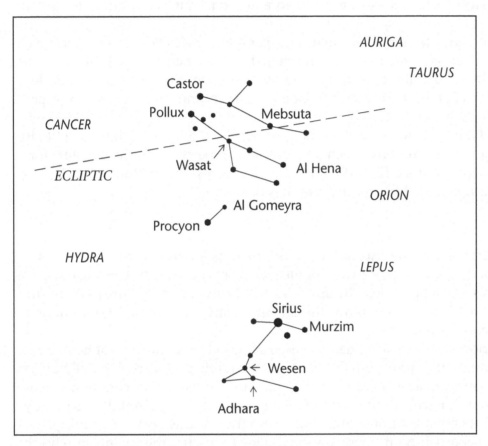

Sirius has a companion star, Sirius B, the "pup." Called a white dwarf star, it is another marvelous wonder of God's creation. Its mass is almost equal to our Sun, but its diameter is fifty times smaller. Its density (mass divided by volume) is 90,000 times that of the Sun, or 125,000 times that of water. One cubic inch weighs about 5,000 pounds (2.5 tons)! A bucket full of Sirius B would weigh 13,000 tons, the weight of the 36 story Saturn 5 rocket that sent the astronauts to the Moon. A cupful of Sirius B would weigh as much as two cement trucks. A lollipop would equal the weight of an automobile.

What causes white dwarf stars? All stars, like our Sun, are nuclear furnaces. Stars produce tremendous heat because of the nuclear conversion of hydrogen into helium. Once the hydrogen "fuel" is consumed, the nuclear reaction stops. The star then begins to contract. As it does so, its density increases at an exponential rate.

Many ancient cultures worshiped Sirius as a god. In Egypt, it was known as the Star of Isis or the Nile Star. Its heliacal rising just before dawn in summer (June 25) signified the annual flooding of the Nile River, upon which Egyptian agriculture and resultantly all of Egyptian life, depended.

Other names given this star are the Sparkling One, Scorching, Dog Star,[110] Star of Autumn, Prince, Leader of the host of heaven, and the Chief of the host. The last three names are the older meanings.

Its scientific name is Alpha Canis Majoris, a member of the constellation Canis Major, the Dog. The name of this constellation in Egyptian is Apes, meaning "the head" and it was pictured, not as a dog, but as a hawk. In Persia, it was pictured as Zeeb, a wolf, meaning "leader, coming quickly."

---

109.   Martha Evans Martin and Donald Howard Menzel, *The Friendly Stars* (New York: Dover Publications, 1964 [1907]), p. 63.

110.   Some cultures believed that, in the summer, Sirius (high in the daytime sky) added to the heat of the Sun. The phrase, "dog days of summer," comes from this ancient association.

Three other stars in Canis Major deserve note. Murzim, Beta Canis Majoris, is a white star with a magnitude of 1.98. It is 750 light-years away and it means "herald of the prince." Wesen, Delta Canis Majoris, is a yellowish-white star with a magnitude of 1.82. It is 2,100 light-years away and means "the bright, the shining." Adhara, Epsilon Canis Majoris, is a bluish-white star with a magnitude of 1.49, the twenty-second brightest star in the sky. It is 680 light-years away and means "the glorious."

Procyon is on the third vertex of the Great Winter Triangle. This star, Alpha Canis Minoris, has a slight tinge of yellow in it. With a magnitude of 0.35, it is the eighth brightest star in the sky. It is 11.3 light-years away. In the Greek, Procyon means "before the dog," but its ancient name meant "redeemer."

Ancient Egyptians called Canis Minor *Sebak*, meaning "conqueror, victorious." The ancients named Beta Canis Minoris *Al Gomeisa*, meaning "the burdened, loaded, bearing." It is bluish-white with a magnitude of 2.84. It is 210 light-years away. Two other stars in this constellation are Al Shira, meaning "prince or chief of left hand," and Al Gomeyra, meaning "who completes or perfects."

Note that the pictures of a dog, hawk, or wolf do not portray the meaning of the stars of these two constellations. The original pictures have been lost, but we can perceive, in the ancient star meanings, a possible portrayal of Christ. He is the Prince of all princes, the glorious One, the Redeemer who has come to complete and perfect the purposes of God.

The Twins of Gemini

Looking straight up from Procyon, we encounter two bright stars separated by 4°. These are commonly known as Castor and Pollux, the "twins" of the constellation Gemini. The ancient Egyptian star maps identified this constellation as Clusus or Clastrum Hor, meaning "the place of Him who cometh." In Coptic, it was Pi-maki, meaning "the united." Both the Hebrew, Thaumin, and the Arabic, Al Tauman, mean "united" also.

In the Greco-Roman period, Castor and Pollux were used as "good luck" charms for navigators. The apostle Paul sailed on an Alexandrian ship that had on its figurehead Castor and Pollux (Acts 28:11). They were also frequently depicted on the coins of this era. These ancients commonly swore by Castor and Pollux. In English Elizabethan literature, the expression "Oh, Gemini!" frequently occurs. Some modern speakers have corrupted this phrase into the profane oath, "By Jiminy!"

Pollux, the lower star, is yellowish-orange with a magnitude of 1.16. It is the seventeenth brightest star in the sky and its computed distance is 35 light-years. Although it is a little brighter than its twin, Castor, it has been traditionally designated as Beta Geminorium. The Greeks named it Hercules, which means "who cometh to suffer."

Castor, Alpha Geminorium, is a white star with a magnitude of 1.59. It is the twenty-third brightest star in the sky and is 45 light-years away. Apollo is its other name, meaning "ruler, judge."

Al Hena, Gamma Geminorium, means "to wound or afflict." It is a white star with magnitude 1.93 and a computed distance of 105 light-years. Delta Geminorium is also known as Wasat, meaning "set." Yellowish-white in color with a magnitude of 3.51, its computed distance is 53 light-years. Mebsuta, Epsilon Geminorium, means "treading under foot." It is a yellow star with magnitude of 2.98. It is 1,000 light-years away. Other stars are Propus (Eta Geminorium) meaning "the branch," Al Giauza, meaning "the palm branch," and Al Dira, meaning "the seed or branch."

The stars of Gemini might speak of Christ as the God-man; the union of God and man. He came to Earth to suffer and is the ruler and judge of all men.

The Good Shepherd

From Castor and Pollux, we look to the west and up towards our zenith. Here we find the sixth brightest star (magnitude of 0.06) in the sky and the second brightest summer star, Capella, the "Goat Star." Golden yellow in color, it is a binary with a computed distance of 45 light-years. Its companion star lies very near, and both whirl about each other with incredible speed. It takes about one hundred days (one-third Earth year) for each to revolve around the other. What is more incredible is that over one hundred of our Suns could fit into the diameter of the orbit over which these companion stars spin!

In Hebrew, it was known as Alioth, meaning "she goat." It is a member of the constellation Auriga, the Hebrew root of which means "the shepherd." According to ancient pictures, Capella is located in the body of a goat resting in the lap of the shepherd. The second brightest star in this constellation is Menkalinan meaning "chain of the goats." It is a white, variable star with a magnitude close to 1.9. Its distance is 90 light-years.

Note that in the most ancient star maps, all of the men are portrayed as shepherds and most of the animals as goats or sheep. The Scripture describes Christ as the Good Shepherd and those who follow Him are identified as sheep.

Taurus, the Bull

This constellation is northwest of Orion. It contains two famous star clusters, the V-shaped Hyades and Pleiades, the seven sisters. In Egypt, this constellation was known as Isis, meaning "who saves or delivers," or Apis, meaning "the head or chief." It is pictured in the act of pushing or rushing. The Hebrews had three designations for it: Reem, meaning "exaltation," Ramah, meaning "high place," and Shur, mean-

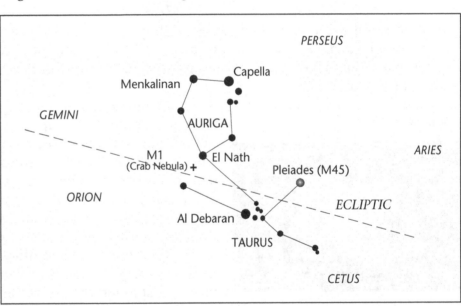

Figure 4–8: Taurus and Auriga

ing "coming, ruling." In the Old Testament (Numbers 2:18), the standard for the tribe of Ephraim was the head of a bull.[111] Ephraim, meaning doubly fruitful, was the second son of Joseph. The blessing of Moses upon Joseph and his son referred to an ox:

> Let it come [blessings] to the head of Joseph, and to the crown of the head of the one distinguished among his brothers. As the firstborn of his ox, majesty is his, and his horns are the horns of the wild ox; with them he shall push his peoples, all at one, to the ends of the earth. And those are the ten thousands of Ephraim... (Deuteronomy 33:16–17).

Before we detail its two clusters, we will note a star on the point of its lower horn, El Nath, or Beta Tauri. It is bluish-white with a magnitude of 1.65. El Nath lies about 3° from the central line of the Milky Way. This position makes it the closest bright star pointing to the galactic anti-center.

---

111. Alfred Edersheim, *The Bible History: Old Testament* (Grand Rapids: William B. Eerdmans Publishing Company 1976 [1886]), p. 151.

This point in the sky is exactly opposite to the hub of our galaxy located in the constellation Sagittarius. Its computed distance is 300 light-years and means "wounded, slain." In the ancient culture of Mithras,[112] the sacrifice of a bull was its central rite symbolizing the "god who redeemed the world."

Granting an exquisite vista through a pair of binoculars (about 2° wide), the Pleiades cluster (M45) moves together through space as a group indicating a binding gravitational force. Job knew this fact over four thousand years ago as God asked him (Job 38:31), "Can you bind the chains of the Pleiades?" As a group, they are about 500 light-years distant. The Greeks named Pleiades "Seven Sisters." This cluster contains, not seven, but over 500 stars! In Hebrew, it means "gathering, the congregation of the judge or ruler." It is mentioned, along with Orion, again in Job 9:9 and Amos 5:8. Its brightest star, with a magnitude of 2.86, is Alcyone, meaning "the center" or "the bright one" or "the leading one of the congregation." Again, Tennyson's *Locksley Hall* contains the most exquisite tribute to the Pleiades found in English literature:

Figure 4–9: The Pleiades cluster

> *Many a night I saw the Pleiads,*
> *rising thro' the mellow shade,*
> *Glitter like a swarm of fireflies*
> *tangled in a silver braid.*

The stars of the Hyades form a distinct V-shaped figure. Each side of the V is about 4°. Hyades means "congregated." Many ancient cultures called this group the "rainy stars" because their rise in the east introduced the rain-filled autumn season. It is the closest cluster of stars with a computed distance of 130 light-years.

Figure 4–10: M1

Located near this cluster is the famed Crab Nebula[113] (M1), the remnant of a supernova, a colossal star explosion. According to a Chinese account, the precise date of this explosion was July 4, 1054. It was visible in the daytime for months and at night for years. Modern photographs, made thirty-four years apart, suggest that the nebulous filaments of M1 are still expanding. Astronomers have spent more time studying this nebula than any other object in the heavens.

The brightest star (magnitude of 0.86) in the Hyades cluster is the orange-colored Al Debaran, Alpha Tauri. It is one of the few first magnitude stars that the Moon occults. Occultation (means "to hide") occurs when a celestial body passes directly in front of another. In 1978, twelve such eclipses of this star occurred. Because the Moon lacks an atmosphere, the disappearance of this star behind it is startlingly abrupt; a nearly instantaneous phenomena.

Al Debaran (in Arabic it is Al Dabaran or Na'ir al Dabaran) means "the follower" or "the Bright One of the follower." In Babylonian lands, this star was known as Ikuu, the "Leading Star of stars." The Hindus knew it as Sataves, the "Leader of the Western Stars." In the second century A.D., the astronomer Ptolemy denoted it by a word that means "the torchbearer." It is 68 light-years away. In the words of Martha E. Martin, "In his section of the sky Aldebaran reigns throughout all the lovely autumn evenings, with beautiful Capella in her own realm to the north of him and Fomalhaut far to the south.[114]

---

112.   Mithraism was a major religion of the Roman Empire and an early rival of Christianity.
113.   This nebula is 5' (' = minutes) wide and its distance from Earth is calculated to be about 4,000 light-years.
114.   Martin, p. 50.

The Christ picture given by Taurus could portray Him as the *Savior* who is the head and chief of His church, His congregated ones. Of Christ, the Lion of the tribe of Judah, Jacob prophesied that "to Him shall be the obedience of the peoples" (Genesis 49:10).

The Spring Stars

Leo

Leo, the Lion, officially heralds the coming of spring. Its brightest star, Regulus, rises due east at 9 P.M. in early January. The Egyptians called this constellation Pi Mentekeon, meaning "pouring out." The Hebrews called it Arieh, meaning "hunting down its prey" and referred to Regulus as the "kingly star" as did the Greeks and Romans. In Syriac, it is Aryo, meaning "the rending lion." In Arabic, it is Al Asad, meaning "a lion coming vehemently, leaping forth as a flame." Medieval Christians regarded Leo as a symbol of the lion's den of Daniel 6. The Hebrews called Leo the "constellation of the kings" and used the Lion walking on blood-red ground as the banner symbol for the tribe of Judah (Numbers 2:3).[115]

Figure 4–11: Leo

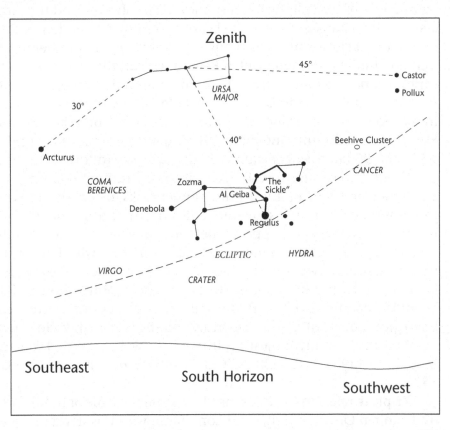

> Judah, your brothers shall praise you; Your hand shall be on the neck of your enemies; Your father's sons shall bow down to you. Judah is a lion's whelp [cub]; from the prey, my son, you have gone up. He crouches, he lies down as a lion, and as a lion, who dares rouse him up? The scepter shall not depart from Judah, nor the ruler's staff from between his feet, until Shiloh comes, and to him shall be the obedience of the peoples. He ties his foal to the vine, and his donkey's colt to the choice vine; He washes his garments in wine, and his robes in the blood of grapes. His eyes are darker than wine, and his teeth are whiter than milk (Genesis 49:8–12).

Alpha Leonis is known today as Regulus, the diminutive form of the Latin *rex*, meaning "little king." The astronomer Nicholaus Copernicus (1473–1543) translated Ptolemy's Greek word for this star (βασιλισκος or "king") into this Latin derivative. In Arabia, it was known as Maliky, "the kingly one." The ancient Babylonians called it Sharru, "the king." The Hindus called it Magha meaning "mighty" or the "Great One." The Persians denoted this star as Miyan, "the Central One." Many ancient cultures refer to this star by words meaning "heart of the lion." According to Frances Rolleston, the ancients also used words that spoke of the judgment action of this kingly star "treading under foot" his enemies. In the ancient star charts, the lion figure is depicted as leaping forth to tear its prey, the serpent Hydra. The universal testimony of all cultures associates this star with royalty and kingly power.

---

115. Edersheim, p. 151.

Regulus is bluish-white in color with a magnitude of 1.36. It is 85 light-years away. Regulus also forms the base, the handle-end, of an interesting asterim called the Sickle, a pattern of six stars that looks like a reversed question mark.

Regulus is very close to another imaginary line on the Celestial Sphere. Delta Orionis is close to the Celestial Equator and this star is close to the Ecliptic. The Ecliptic represents the path that the Sun traces across the Celestial Sphere. The Moon and the planets (except Pluto) are always seen within 8–9° of the Ecliptic because they all revolve around the Sun in one plane. Therefore, when a star like Regulus is close to the Ecliptic, conjunctions often occur with planets. A conjunction is an apparent close approach of one celestial object to another as seen from Earth. On July 7, 1959, Venus actually passed in front of Regulus (occultation), an exceedingly rare event. A couple of centuries will pass before Venus will again occult a first magnitude star.

Other bright stars in Leo are Denebola (white, magnitude of 2.14, and 43 light-years distant), in the Lion's tail, meaning "the Judge or Lord who cometh," Zozma (white, magnitude of 2.55, and 80 light-years distant), meaning "shining forth or wise one," and Al Geiba (orange, magnitude of 1.98, and 90 light-years distant), meaning "the exaltation."

About 2° to the northwest of Al Geiba is the radiant point[116] of the famous Leonid Meteor showers. A meteor is a rock, smaller than larger rocks (asteroids) and at least as large as a speck of dust, that has moved through space and entered Earth's atmosphere. A meteor shower consists of a large number of meteors that appear together and seem to come from the same area in the sky. As each meteoroid[117] is heated to incandescence by friction with Earth's atmosphere, they make a bright trail or streak in the night sky. Like clockwork, the Leonid showers appear in the sky every November in the early morning hours. The English poet John Milton (1608–1674) may have referred to the Leonids when he said, "Swift as a shooting star in autumn thwarts the night." These showers can be so grandiose that they can literally "fill the sky" with vivid trails of greenish or bluish streaks.[118]

We can see many majestic spiral galaxy systems in this constellation. Among these are M65, M66, M95, M96, NGC 3628, NGC 3193 (elliptical), NGC 3187, NGC 3185, NGC 2903, and NGC 3521.

Scripture refers to Christ as the "Lion from the tribe of Judah" (Revelation 5:5). He is the glorious and exalted One, the Judge and Lord of all, who has tread the enemy under His foot.

Virgo

At 9 P.M., in mid March, the bluish-white Spica rises in the east. It is the sixteenth brightest star in the sky with a magnitude of 1.00. Its computed distance is 275 light-years.

Spica is a member of the constellation Virgo, the virgin. The Hebrews called this group of stars Bethulah, meaning "a virgin." The Arabic word for this constellation is very similar to this Hebrew word and it means "branch." In the ancient star charts, Virgo is pictured with a branch in her right hand. In Latin, *Virgo* means "virgin" and *Virga* means "branch."

Because Virgo heralds the coming of autumn (harvest time) when it disappears in the western horizon just after the Sun, many ancient cultures associated this constellation with womanhood and fertility. The ancient Egyptians linked this constellation with Isis, the Divine wife and mother. In Assyria, she was "the wife of Bel." In Babylonian lands, she was Ishtar, the Queen of the stars and of fertility, identified in I Kings 11:5, 33 as Ashtoreth. The ancient Greeks identified it as Ceres, the goddess of harvest and fruitfulness, of all living things that grow on land. The English Benedictine Monk and Scholar Bede (673?–735) noted that the Saxons associated Virgo with their goddess

---

116. The apparent celestial origin of a meteoric shower.
117. A *meteoroid* is a small body of rock or metal traveling through space that, upon entering Earth's atmosphere, is heated to glowing and becomes a *meteor*.
118. According to a contemporary print, on November 13, 1833, the Leonid showers were so numerous and concentrated that the entire sky lighted up with them!

Eoestre or Eostre.[119] This name still survives in our modern nomenclature as Easter. Medieval Christians saw this constellation as representing the Madonna or as "Ruth of the Fields" from the Old Testament book of Ruth.

Spica was known anciently as Al Zimach, meaning "the branch, or an ear of corn." Virgo was pictured by the ancients holding a spike of wheat in her left hand. In Hebrew, Spica was known as Tsemech, meaning "the branch." Spica is also near the Ecliptic and is therefore involved in many conjunctions.

Figure 4–12: Virgo and Boötes

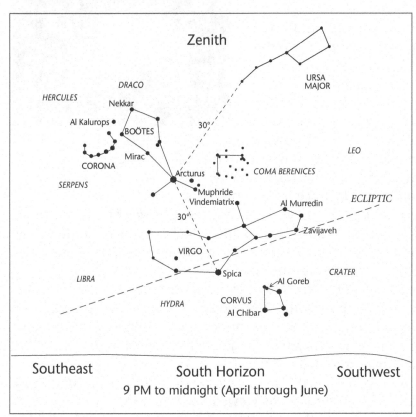

9 PM to midnight (April through June)

Figure 4–13: M104

The other stars in Virgo are not very bright. Zavijaveh, Beta Virginis, means "the gloriously beautiful." Al Mureddin means "who shall come down or who shall have dominion." Al Mureddin in Chaldee is *Vindemiatrix* which means "the son, branch, or who cometh."

Virgo contains a clustered wonderland of galaxies. For sighting them, astronomers recommend at least a six-inch reflector telescope. Two beautiful elliptical systems are M84 and M86. Some spiral systems are NGC 4388, NGC 4216, NGC 4567 & 4568 (The "Siamese Twins"), NGC 5364, M58, M90, M61, and M104 (The Sombrero Galaxy).

Coma Berenices

This constellation is very interesting in that its present name shows us how its ancient meaning has been corrupted. The Greeks named this group of stars after Berenice II of Egypt, queen of Ptolemy III (246–221 B.C.). According to legend, she vowed to offer her hair to the gods if the king would return safely from a battle. When Ptolemy returned safely, she offered the locks of her hair but they mysteriously vanished. Greek legend says that the gods stole her hair and placed it as a constellation in the sky.

Egyptians named this constellation Shesnu, meaning "the desired son." The Hebrews named it Comah, meaning "the desired, the longed for." It was pictured anciently as a virgin with child! In Latin, *Coma* means "hair" and in Greek *Kóme* means the same thing. So, it is easy to see how "the desired one" was changed to "hair."

---

119. This was the Saxon goddess of love, in honor of whom a festival was celebrated in April or Eostermonath.

M53, a rich globular star cluster, appears in Coma Berenices. Several spiral galaxies are also located in the Coma Galaxy cluster[120]: M64 (Black-Eye Galaxy), M99, NGC 4274, NGC 4565 (a famous "edge-on" spiral), NGC 4725, and M100.

Figure 4–14: M100

Boötes

Boötes is anciently pictured with a spear in the right hand and a sickle in the left hand. The Egyptians called this constellation Smat, meaning "the one who rules, subdues, governs." They also called it Bau, meaning "the coming one."

Its brightest star is the famed Arcturus, which means "he cometh." This is the same star whose bright rays flowed down upon the righteous Job more than two thousand six hundred years ago (Job 9:9; 38:32).[121] To him, this star revealed the wonders of his Creator. Golden yellow in color and the size of 25 billion Earths, it is the fourth brightest star in the sky (magnitude of -0.06). It rises with Spica (a little to the north) at 9 P.M. in the middle of March. Its computed distance is 36 light-years.

In 1933, its computed distance was forty light-years. In that year, its light was focused through a telescope onto a photocell that tripped the floodlights thus opening the "Century of Progress" exposition in Chicago, Illinois. The organizers of this exposition believed that this light left Arcturus in 1893 (forty years before) when Chicago hosted a similar fair.

This star is distinctive on two other counts. First, in 1635, it was the very first star ever seen in broad daylight through a telescope. You can duplicate this feat today by properly aligning the setting circles[122] of a good small telescope. If you set these circles correctly, you will be able to see Arcturus in broad daylight! Second, instead of rotating around the galactic center along the galactic equatorial plane, this star rotates perpendicular to this plane.

Two deep sky objects of note in Boötes are NGC 5248 (spiral galaxy) and NGC 5614. NGC 5614 is an unusual spiral galaxy in that it looks like a tornado as viewed from the top.

Other stars in Boötes are Al Kalurops, meaning "the branch, treading under foot," Muphride, meaning "who separates," Nekkar (in the head), meaning "pierced," and Mirac or Mizr, meaning "the coming forth as an arrow, preserving, guarding."

These stars and their meanings are summarized in Psalm 96:

> Let the heavens be glad, and let the earth rejoice; let the sea roar, and all it contains; let the field exult, and all that is in it. Then all the trees of the forest will sing for joy before the Lord, for He is coming; for He is coming to judge the earth. He will judge the world in righteousness, and the peoples in His faithfulness (Psalm 96:11–13).

Corona Borealis

Corona Borealis is Latin for Northern Crown. In Hebrew, it is Atarah, meaning "a royal crown." In Arabic, it is Al Iclil, meaning "an ornament, or jewel." Its brightest star is Al Phecca, a white star with magnitude of 2.23. It is 75 light-years away and it means "the shining."

Some astronomers call the Corona galaxy cluster a "super galaxy." It is remarkable in that it contains more than 400 galaxies, most of them elliptical systems, and that all of them are concentrated in an area of the sky that is one-half a degree wide (the apparent width of the Moon)!

---

120.   This galaxy cluster has approximately 1,000 galaxies in it, all at the distance of about 368 million light-years.

121.   Some scholars say that this word (*Ayish* in Hebrew) denotes the constellation Ursa Major, the "Great Bear."

122.   These are circular disks, two to a set, one for declination marked in degrees and the other for right ascension marked in hours and minutes. See Sam Brown, *All About Telescopes* (Barrington, NJ: Edmund Scientific Company, 1975), pp. 33–37.

This constellation could speak of Christ, after he tasted death for all men, who was crowned with glory and honor (Hebrews 2:9).

Corvus

Four stars of magnitude 3.0 make up a small quadrangle, known commonly as "Spica's Spanker" or anciently as Corvus, the crow (or raven). The Egyptians knew it as Herna, meaning "the breaking of the enemy." Three of its stars are Al Chibar, meaning "the curse inflicted"; Al Goreb, meaning "the raven"; and Mincher al Goreb, meaning "the raven tearing to pieces." The Ring-tail galaxy (NGC 4038), a peculiar shaped spiral structure, is a noted deep sky object in Corvus.

Corvus is pictured as pecking away at Hydra, the serpent. It could picture Christ in judgment breaking up the enemy by inflicting a curse upon him.

The Summer Stars

Scorpio

This constellation is a most distinct and striking summer sight. At 9 P.M. in late July, it is due south hugging the horizon.[123] It sets in the west at 9 P.M. in September and October. It is grouped around three other constellations: Ophiuchus, Serpens, and Corona Borealis. Ophiuchus is anciently pictured as preventing Serpens, the serpent, from attaining Corona, the crown, and crushing with his foot Scorpio, the scorpion. In this light, Ophiuchus may picture Christ in His triumph over the vain attempts of Satan to take away His crown. Two of these attempts are

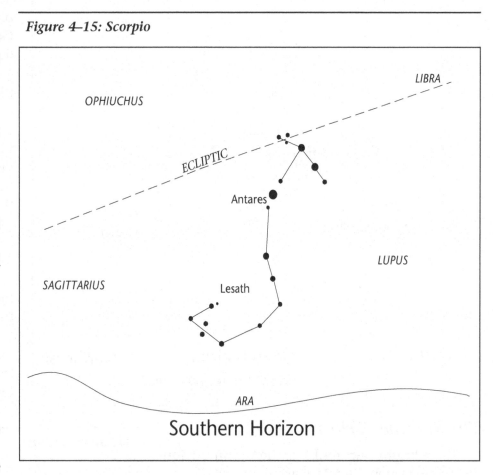

Figure 4–15: Scorpio

OPHIUCHUS
LIBRA
ECLIPTIC
Antares
SAGITTARIUS
Lesath
LUPUS
ARA
Southern Horizon

described in Exodus 1 and Matthew 2. Revelation 12 gives a symbolic summary of the conflict between the dragon and Christ.

An ancient Babylonian title for this constellation was Bilu-sha-zieri, "The Lord of the seed." This may be a perversion of Genesis 3:15 where the seed of the woman is depicted as crushing the head of the serpent. The Egyptians named it Isidis, meaning "the attack of the enemy or oppression." The symbol of the scorpion is one of the oldest of the Egyptian hieroglyphics; in fact, in 3,000 B.C., the Pharaoh Ip was called "The Scorpion King." The sacred star of the Egyptian goddess Isis was

---

123. In Job 9:9, the "chambers of the south" may refer to this constellation, the great sky spaces of the Southern Hemisphere, or to Crux, the Southern Cross.

Antares. The Arabs named it Al Akrab, meaning "wounding him who cometh." A number of early Greek temples were oriented to the rising of Antares including the temple at Corinth and the first Temple of Apollo at Delphi. The Hebrews also identified Scorpio as Akrab, meaning "the conflict or war." The ancients, however, commonly drew this constellation as an Eagle. The tribal emblem of Dan was an Eagle on bright yellow ground (Numbers 2:25).[124] The blessing of Dan's father, Jacob, connects the Eagle symbol to the serpent:

> Dan shall be a serpent in the way, a horned snake in the path, that bites the horse's heels, so that his rider falls backward (Genesis 49:17).

Figure 4–16: Northern Summer Sky

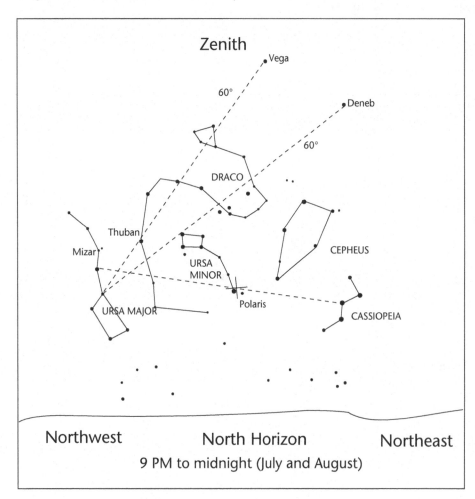

9 PM to midnight (July and August)

Antares is Scorpio's brightest star. Rising at 9 P.M. in the southeast in late May, its red glow signifies the coming of summer. Therefore, it is often mistaken for Mars, the red planet. Because of this, the Greek astronomer Ptolemy defined it as the "rival of Mars." It has two "companion" stars in its outline. The magnitude of Antares is 0.92 and its computed distance is 420 light-years. Its diameter is approximately 600 million miles, 700 times greater than our Sun. The ancient meaning of Antares was "the wounding." On its "sting" is Lesath, a bluish-white star of magnitude 2.71, having the meaning "perverse."

Many star clusters appear in Scorpio. Among these are M4, M6, M7, M62, M80, and NGC 6231.

The Summer Triangle

Three bright stars make up the Summer Triangle: Vega, Deneb, and Al Tair.

Vega rises in the northeast at 9 P.M. in late May. It is a member of the constellation Lyra, the harp. In Latin, *Lyra* means "lyric poetry" or "poetry set to stringed instrumental music." A lyra was a harp used by the ancients. It can be easily recognized by the fact that four stars next to it form

Figure 4–17: Lyra

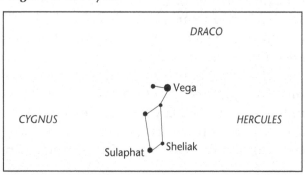

124.   Edersheim, p. 151.

an oblique parallelogram. Its color is a vivid blue blaze making it a marvel of beauty and elegance. It is 26 light-years distant.

Due to the precession of Earth's axis (see Appendix Eleven), Vega will be the Pole star in the year A.D. 12,000. At that time it will be 4.5° from true north. It is now 51° distant. Earth travels around the Sun at an approximate rate of twenty miles per second. The speed of every object within the Milky Way around the galactic center is about 180 miles per second. The planet Earth, along with our Solar System, is also traveling at approximately twelve miles per second toward a place in space now occupied by Vega. This position is called the apex of the Sun's path in space or simply the solar apex.

Figure 4–18: The Summer Triangle

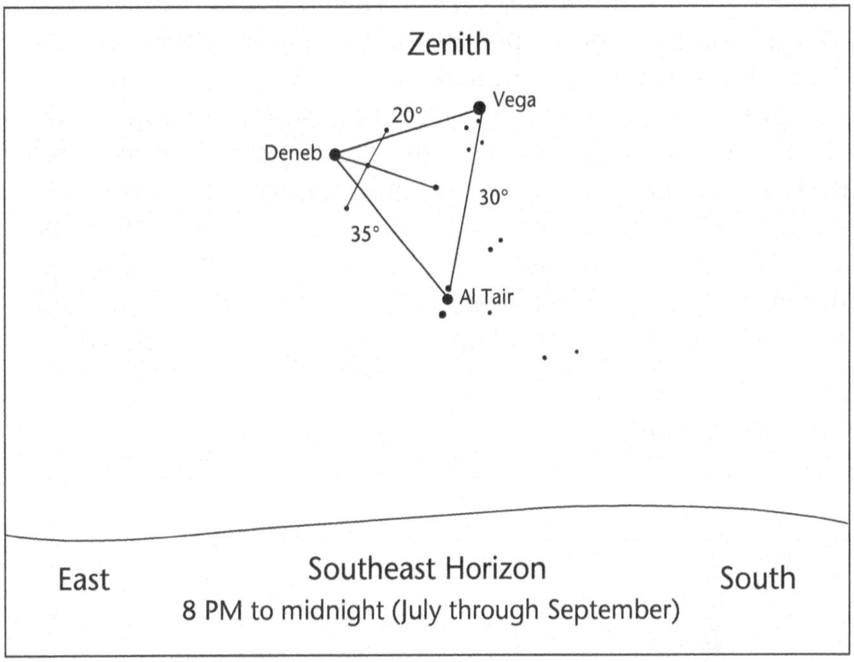

On the night of July 16–17, 1850, astronomers at the Harvard Observatory focused their sights upon Vega and made, by the daguerreotype process, the first photograph of a star. They used a 15-inch refractor telescope with an exposure of 100 seconds.

Among the Romans, Vega was the "harp-star." Other cultures named it the eagle or vulture star. To these civilizations, these birds symbolized the subjugation of an enemy. The Babylonians called it Dilgan, the "messenger of light." The Akkadians called it Tiranna, the "life of heaven." The Assyrians named it Dayana-same, the "judge of heaven." Combining the bird symbolism with this ancient star nomenclature indicates that this star could speak of the themes of exaltation, triumph, and victory. Two stars on the "strings" of the "harp" are Sheliak, meaning "eagle," and Sulaphat, meaning "springing up, or ascending." The ancient Egyptians named this constellation Tent-kar, "the serpent ruled."

Figure 4–19: Cygnus

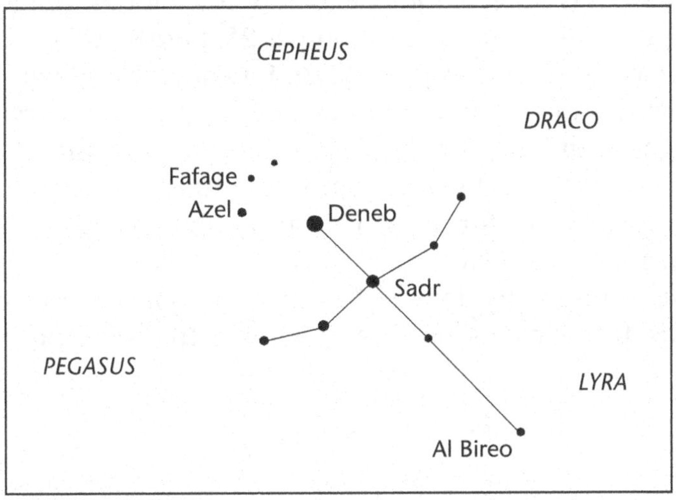

This constellation could point to the ascension and resulting exaltation of Christ. Like an eagle soaring the heavenly heights, Christ rules over all, including Satan, the serpent. Is it not significant, then, that the apex of our Solar System, the path to which we are headed in space, means exaltation and triumph? Is not history, according to the Bible, moving toward the same goal of the consummated exaltation, triumph, and victory of the Lord Jesus Christ (see Hebrews 1:13; 10:13; I Corinthians 15:20–28)?

You can see Deneb, meaning "the judge," rising in the northeast in early June at 9 P.M. It is the nineteenth brightest star in the sky (magnitude of 1.26) and its computed distance is 1,600 light-years. It is a supergiant star equaled in luminosity[125] only by Rigel. Deneb belongs to the constellation Cygnus, a variation of the Latin for "swan."[126] In Arabia, this constellation was called "The Flying Eagle." Because this constellation looks like a cross, medieval Christians called it the Northern Cross. During the Christmas season, this cross assumes a vertical position as it sets in the western sky. Deneb is also denoted as the "Great Star of the Cross."

Cygnus lies in a dense part of the Milky Way where a myriad of small stars forms a backdrop to its brilliant luster. The entire region is a gold mine of wonders for binocular viewing.

The ancient Egyptians called Deneb Tes-ark, meaning "this from afar" or "hindmost." In the beak of Cygnus, we find the beautiful, binary star Al Bireo (meaning "flying quickly"). One star is deep blue and the other bright orange. It has a magnitude of 3.09 and is 410 light-years away. Sadr, meaning "who returns as in a circle," is at the base of the neck. Yellowish-white, its magnitude is 2.23 and its computed distance is 750 light-years. In the tail is Azel and Fafage, meaning "who goes and returns quickly," and "gloriously shining forth" respectively. This constellation could picture Christ as the coming judge, both in present circumstances and at the end of time.

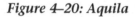

Figure 4–20: Aquila

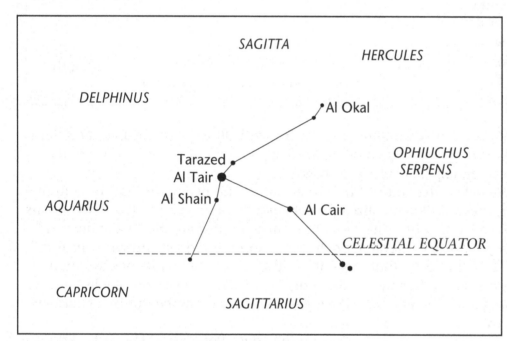

Not far from Deneb lies 61 Cygni, eleven light-years away. In 1838, Friedrich Wilhelm Bessel (1784–1846) chose this star for the first successful attempt to measure the actual distance of a star by trigonometry (see Appendix Seven). Cygnus contains two beautiful, lace-like nebulae, NGC 6960 and NGC 6992. Together, astronomers call these striking objects the "Bridal Veil Nebula."

Al Tair rises due east at 9 P.M. in the late June. White in color, it is the twelfth brightest star in the sky with a magnitude of 0.77. Its computed distance is sixteen light-years. It is noted for its rapid rotation speed making one turn per 6.5 hours. Our Sun makes one rotation per 25.4 days. Al Tair, which means "the wounding," is a member of the constellation Aquila, Latin for eagle. It has two "companion" stars like Antares: Al Shain, a yellowish star with a magnitude of 3.71 (40 light-years away), and Tarazed, an orange star with a magnitude of 2.67 (300 light-years away). Al Shain, in Arabic, means "the bright." Its root, in Hebrew, means scarlet covered (compare with Joshua 2:18). Tarazed means "wounded, torn." Using the two companion stars of Al Tair as pointers, Vega is about one and one-half to two handspans upward towards the observer's zenith.

Other stars in this constellation are Al Cair, meaning "the piercing," and Al Okal, meaning "wounded in the heel." From the above meanings, this constellation could point to the sufferings of Christ on the Cross of Calvary.

---

125. 60,000 times that of the Sun.
126. *Cycnus* is Latin for "swan."

The Autumn Stars

Piscis Australis

Piscis Australis means "Southern Fish." It is about 6.5 hours (98°) behind Scorpio and rises in the southeast at 9 P.M. in the middle of September.

Its brightest star, rising in the southeast at 9 P.M. in early July, is Fomalhaut. It is white, has a magnitude of 1.17 (the eighteenth brightest star in the sky), and is 23 light-years away. Fomal-

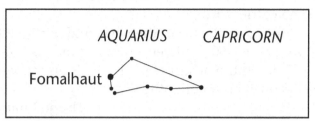

Figure 4–21: Piscis Australia

haut comes from the Arabic, Fum al Haut, which means "the mouth of the fish."

In ancient Egypt, Piscis Australis was known as Aar, meaning "a stream." This constellation is anciently pictured receiving the water poured from Aquarius. Two biblical pictures could be derived from the Aquarius and Piscis Australis constellations. One could refer to the living waters of the Holy Spirit poured out upon all flesh because of Christ's victorious enthronement (see John 7:37–39, Acts 2:33, and Revelation 22:1–2). The other could refer to the bowls of judgment poured out upon God's enemies (Revelation 16:1)

Pegasus

This constellation is identified by its distinctive group of four, faint stars that form a square, called the "Square of Pegasus." It is usually pictured in ancient star maps as a winged horse. *Pega* means "the chief," and *sus* means "the horse." The horse is actually upside-down with its head located in the lower right portion of the constellation. Pegasus is quite large in its scope (each side measures 15° in length) and is clearly seen from September to December.

Three of the four stars of the square officially belong to Pegasus. The fourth, upper left, belongs to Andromeda.

Markab, the lower

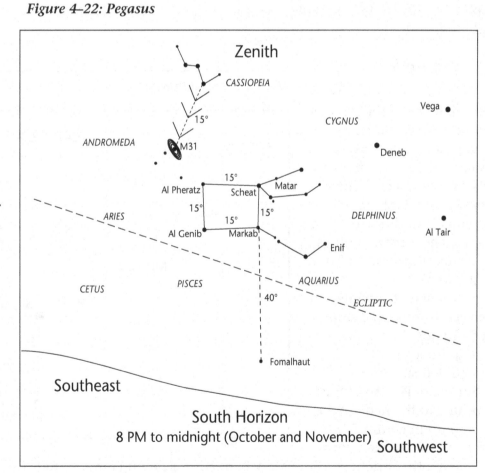

Figure 4–22: Pegasus

right star of the square, is located on the neck of the horse. It is white, has a magnitude of 2.5 and is 110 light-years away. It means "returning from afar."

Scheat, the upper right star of the square, is located on the front foreleg of the horse. It is a red variable with a magnitude of 2.5. Its computed distance is 210 light-years and it means "who goeth and returneth."

Al Genib, the lower left star of the square, is located on the tip of the wing of the horse. It is bluish-white, has a magnitude of 2.84, and is computed to be at a distance of 570 light-years. It means "who carries away."

Matar, on the leg of the horse and northwest of Sheat, is yellow in color, has a magnitude of 2.96, and is 360 light-years away. It means "who causes to overflow."

Enif, on the nostril of the horse, is an orange star, has a magnitude of 2.31, and is 780 light-years away. It means "the water."

The globular star cluster M15, a rich and compact arrangement, is found in Pegasus. The spiral galaxy NGC 7331 also appears in this constellation. It is a system similar in type and size to the Milky Way. Other spiral galaxies are NGC 7814 (edge-on), NGC 7479, NGC 7217.

This constellation may refer to the coming again of Christ in the person of the Holy Spirit (see John 14:1–3, 16–18). He is the One who brings the water of life to us. Or, it could refer to the waters of judgment.

Figure 4–23: NGC 7331

Figure 4–24: M15

Andromeda

This constellation is best known by the famous galaxy named after it. Egyptians called this constellation Set, which means "set up as queen." The Hebrews called it Sirra, which means "the chained." Other names carry meanings such as "the afflicted," and "the weak."

Al Pheratz, a white star with a computed distance of 120 light-years and a magnitude of 2.06, is the upper left star in the "Square of Pegasus." It is located in the head of the "woman in chains." It means "the broken down."

Figure 4–25: Andromeda

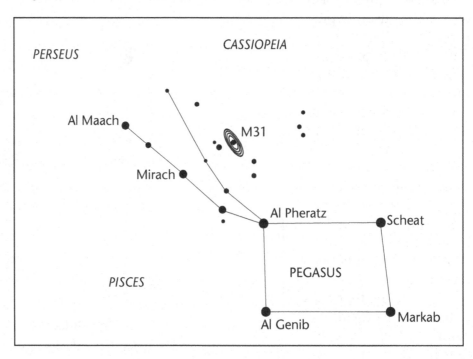

Two other bright stars are Mirach, a red star having a magnitude of 2.03 and a distance of 75 light-years, and Al Maach, a beautiful binary star, orange in color, magnitude of 2.12, and 260 light-years away. Mirach means "the weak," and Al Maach means "the struck down."

This constellation could possibly refer to either the sufferings of Christ or the sufferings experienced by His bride, the Church (see Philippians 1:29).

The great Andromeda galaxy (M31 or NGC 224), seen as a dim patch of light, concludes our seasonal journey through the night sky. It is the third galaxy, besides the Large Magellanic Cloud and the Small Magellanic Cloud, which the naked eye can see. Its estimated, computed distance is approximately 2,200,000 light-years and its estimated diameter is 200,000 light-years. Not long af-

Figure 4–26: Andromeda Galaxy (M31)

ter M31 rises in the northeast (9 P.M. in late September), we see the rise of Rigel in the southeast. Orion, the great winter constellation, will soon make its presence known and the parade of the stars will repeat itself in orderly fashion for another year.

Questions for Review and Further Study

Short sentence answers:

1. Define the following words:
   a. Zenith
   b. Nadir
   c. Asterim
   d. Dwarf star
   e. Galactic anti-center
   f. Ecliptic
   g. Conjunction
   h. Occultation
   i. Heliacal rising
   j. Precession

2. Which three stars compose the "Great Winter Triangle?"

3. Give two examples of an asterim.

Short essay:

1. Explain the picture revealed by the constellation Orion.

2. Where in Scripture does it speak of the Gemini constellation? Explain why the two stars of this constellation were used as they were in this Scripture passage.

Long essay:

1. Using the meaning of the constellation name and the meaning of individual stars in the constellation, explain how Orion points to Christ.

2. Explain the biblical message revealed through the composite picture of the constellations Scorpio, Ophiuchus, Serpens, and Corona Borealis.

3. Explain how the Greeks corrupted the name and meaning of Coma Berenices.

4. Explain how the following constellations point to the person and work of Christ. Use constellation meanings, pictures, and star-name meanings where applicable.

 a. Leo, the Lion

 b. Virgo, the Virgin

 c. Aquila, the Eagle

 d. Lyra, the Harp

 e. Cygnus, the Swan

Research:

1. Research and report on how to evaluate the light gathering capabilities of a telescope using its *f-ratio.*

2. Research and report on the difference between the altazimuth and equatorial telescope mountings.

3. Do a research project on astrophotography.

Chapter Five

The Zodiac Constellations

In the last chapter, we looked at the most conspicuous constellations and stars of the night sky. We talked about a few constellations (Gemini, Taurus, Leo, Virgo, and Scorpio) that have a special place in astronomical lore. They are members of a twelve-constellation federation called the zodiac.

These constellations are common to every nation and culture of Earth. For example, in A.D. 150, the Greek astronomer Ptolemy said that they were of "unquestioned authority, unknown origin, and unsearchable antiquity."

The word *zodiac* comes from the Greek word *zodiakos*. Its root, *zoad*, is a Hebrew word that means "a way, a step, or a path."[127]

The Ecliptic

We find these constellations on an imaginary line on the Celestial Sphere called the Ecliptic. As Earth revolves around the Sun (in heliocentricity), the Sun appears to carve out a pathway on the celestial sphere. This pathway is the Ecliptic and the zodiac constellations are always located on this path.

The Ecliptic is important for another reason.

Figure 5–1: Constellations in the Sky

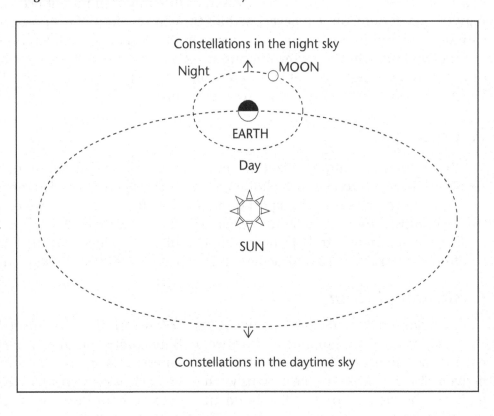

Constellations in the night sky

Night — MOON

EARTH

Day

SUN

Constellations in the daytime sky

---

127. According to Job 38:32, God brings forth the Mazzaroth (zodiac signs) in its season.

As mentioned in Chapter Four, the Moon and the planets are always seen within 8° to 9° of this "line" because they all revolve around the Sun in one plane. The only planet that does not do this is Pluto. If you know how to identify the constellations of the zodiac, then you can spot many planets throughout the year; planets like Mars (fiery red), Jupiter (tinged with yellow), Saturn (decidedly yellow), Venus (white), and Mercury. Because it is so near to the Sun, Mercury is rarely seen at all. When it is visible, it appears as a very bright star. Uranus is barely visible to the naked eye and you will need a telescope to see Neptune and Pluto.

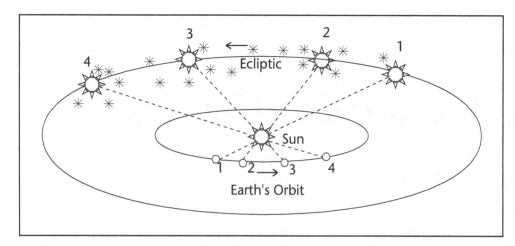

Figure 5–2: The Ecliptic

Venus is never more than about 48° (2.5 handspans—remember, one handspan equals 20°) away from the Sun. When it is seen in the morning, it rises about three hours earlier than the Sun. At night, it sets about three hours after the Sun. Venus is referred to in the Bible three times as the "day star" or "morning star" (see II Peter 1:19; Revelation 2:28; 22:16). The passage in Peter talks about the dawning of the day and the "day star arising in your hearts." Jesus Christ is the Day Star. He first "arises" in the hearts of believers. Then, the day dawns in its full and brilliant light casting out the darkness. The light of God in individual believers heralds the coming light of the gospel of the glory of Christ proclaimed and manifested in a world covered in the darkness of sin (cf. Isaiah 60:1–3).

The Moon makes twelve revolutions around Earth in one year. Its relationship to the zodiac is that it passes through each of the twelve constellations during the year. That is, every month, the Full Moon will be in another zodiac constellation.

Astrology

The cultures of antiquity identified not only the twelve constellations of the zodiac, but thirty-six others. For each zodiac constellation, these ancient peoples added three complimentary constellations called decans (meaning part or piece); therefore, the night sky could be separated into twelve groups of four constellations each, or a total of forty-eight.

The birthplace of astrology, according to biblical scholars, was the kingdom of Babel. Study carefully Genesis 10:8–12 and Genesis 11:1–9. Note that these passages are parallel to each other.

Cush, Son of Ham

Cush gathered the people together at Shinar (modern Iraq). He instigated a rebellion against God and initiated the building of the tower of Babel. Babel originally meant "the gate of God"—*bab* means "gate, door" and *el* means "god." Genesis 11:4 speaks of that top of the tower "is the heavens." This phrase can be variously interpreted: (1) it may speak of the height of the tower, (2) it may suggest fear of another flood—an attempt to close the heavens, or (3) the top may have been inscribed with the heavens (the zodiac). The fact that the zodiac is common to all languages and nations could confirm this.

What is certain is their desire to "make a name for themselves." At this point God "comes down" and confuses their languages and scatters them over the face of the world (Genesis 11:5–8). As these people populated the Earth, they carried with them, not only their disobedience, but also their understanding of the zodiac. It should be noted that all languages today (and the zodiac) indicate a common source, so bearing out this account of how the descendants of the three sons of Noah became divided.

Soon after his death, Cush was deified as a man who became a god. In ancient Babylon he was worshipped under the name Bel, meaning "confounder or babbler"[128] (Isaiah 46:1; Jeremiah 50:2; 51:44)—signifying that he was the one who was the cause of the confusion of the languages.

He was also worshipped as Mercury or Hermes (son of Ham). Hermes was known as the interpreter of the gods or the one that makes the gods known.[129] The suggestion here is that he received the endorsement of heaven (which was not the case) in building the tower of Babel.

The god Janus is another god understood to be Cush. This god is depicted as having two faces turned in opposite directions. He is the picture of confusion and called by the ancients Chaos (in the ancient language of Babylon, *Chaos* means "Cush"). The symbol of Janus is a club. The ancient Babylonians understood this symbol to mean "to scatter abroad" or "break in pieces."

Nimrod, Son of Cush

Nimrod (means "little rebel"), son of Cush, continued his father's rebellion by building the city of Babylon. Genesis 10:8 says "he began to be a mighty one on the earth." This phrase may suggest that a struggle was necessary for him to achieve the status of "mighty one."

Genesis 10:9 says that he was "a mighty hunter before the Lord." A "mighty hunter" suggests two possible interpretations: (1) he was the first to train in the hunt thus protecting man from the wild animals—by this he would be looked upon as a protector or savior of mankind or (2) he could have hunted men in order to persecute or oppress them. "Before the Lord" suggests that whatever he hunted, he did these activities defiantly in the presence or sight of God (compare with Genesis 6:11).

Nimrod expanded his conquests (Genesis 10:10–12) and was the first one to build cities and fortifications. Along with his conquests and building programs, he led the nations in rebellion against God corrupting every remembrance of Him. He led the nations of that time to believe that true life can only be found in the gratification of the senses. In ancient representations, feasting, women, and merriment always surround him. Ancient history also indicates that Nimrod married a woman, Semiramis, universally noted for her beauty.

Nimrod's death is shrouded in mystery, but we know it to be a violent one. Legend and mythology join almost with one voice to say that a great enemy of Nimrod slew him with words by the power of God's Spirit in judgment for his violence and rebellion. One source states that his enemy was none other than Shem (or his followers), the son of Noah and the faithful one of the covenant. This is a possibility for Shem lived 500 years after the Flood (Genesis 11:10) and had first hand knowledge of the covenant (Genesis 9:6).

The legends state that the whole world mourned Nimrod's death as one would mourn the savior of mankind. Shem, after the custom of the day (cf. Judges 19:29; I Samuel 11:7), cut up Nimrod's body and sent the pieces to the leaders of the cities as a warning to them. Semiramis then declared Shem to be the great enemy of mankind and that Nimrod's shedding of blood would free the race from this enemy. She declared him Zeroashta (in Chaldean, this word means "seed of the woman"). Note the perverse relationship to Genesis 3:15. She declared that Nimrod had overcome the serpent

---

128. *Bel* is a cognate of *Baal,* meaning "lord" or "husband."
129. We derive the word, hermeneutics, the science and methodology of interpretation (especially of the text of Scripture), from Hermes.

and was now to be worshipped as "God." But, after the action of Shem, such open worship would be impossible and thus began the hidden mystery religion of Babylon.

Semiramis's next step was to place herself among the gods by claiming to give birth to a reincarnated Nimrod. Statues of her with the child at her breast were adored. She was known as Rhea, or the great goddess, the mother of the gods. That religion spread throughout the known world, each nation naming Semiramis and Nimrod according to their language and adding to the myth:

➢ Egypt (Isis and Osiris)

➢ India (Isis and Iswara)

➢ Asia (Cybele and Deoius)

➢ Rome (Fortuna and Jupiter)

➢ Greece (Ceres and Bacchus; Venus and Cupid)

➢ China (Sing Moo and the Child)

Semiramis was known in Asia as Diana or Artemis of the Ephesians (Acts 19:25–28). Jeremiah called her the "queen of heaven" (Jeremiah 7:18; 44:17–25).

Other names by which Nimrod was known are as follows:

➢ Tammuz (Ezekiel 8:14) by the Babylonians

➢ Saturn (hidden one)

➢ Kronos (the mighty one)

➢ Zernebogus (seed of the prophet Cush), the name used by the Anglo-Saxons and known as the representative of the devil in Europe

➢ Khons (god of the hunt) by the Egyptians

➢ Consus or Neptune (hidden one) by the Romans.

Nimrod was symbolized as a centaur with a bow and arrow and adored as the first to hunt with horses and protect mankind. He was also depicted as Atlas, the one who carried the heavens on his shoulders.

The day of his "reincarnation" or "rebirth" to his wife Semiramis was fixed as December 24 and called "Lady Day." December 25 was the birthday of the young god and was called "Child Day." Days in the spring (around Easter) were observed for lamenting and recollecting his death at the hand of Shem.

It is clear from the foregoing that Nimrod was set forth (by the influence of Satan and his host yet under the control of the sovereign God) as an alternative Messiah and was adored by every nation on Earth. It is also quite clear how the zodiac became corrupted with falsehoods based upon the Nimrod/Semiramis legend: e.g., the centaur (Sagittarius, Centaurus), the mighty hunter (Orion), the woman with child (Coma Berenices, Virgo), etc.

This ancient mystery religion reinterpreted Genesis 3:15 in an attempt to deceive the nations into thinking that Nimrod was the true deliverer and savior of the world.[130] The corruption of the

---

130. Note that many of the leaders of the ancient world claimed this Messianic role. For example, Octavian (who ruled Rome from 27 B.C. to A.D. 14) took to himself the title Caesar Augustus (means "reverenced"). This title was considered to be a divine title that made Octavian Zeus incarnate. In various parts of the empire temples were built to the goddess Roma and the god Augustus. Virgil wrote of the "advent" of Augustus declaring, "The turning-point of the ages has come." Ethelbert Stauffer, in his *Christ and the Caesars* (Philadelphia: Westminster Press, 1955) summarized the symbolism of the coins issued in the empire: "Salvation is to be found in none other save Augustus, and there is no other name given to men in which they can be saved." The message that the Apostle Peter preached in Acts 4:12 takes on new light in this context. The message of the Gospel of Christ challenged the Roman Empire at its roots—and Rome knew this all too well; the battle was engaged and, after many centuries of persecution, Rome finally fell to the power of the Gospel.

zodiac was a part of this deception. The scheme of the enemy is to pervert and corrupt. Everything that God created as good the devil tries to subvert. The devil corrupts to prevent man from understanding God's message revealed in His creation. God created the stars to show forth the word concerning His Word, Jesus Christ. God intended the zodiac to declare His glory.

Now that the "light of the nations" has come and that "the veil of darkness" has been lifted by Christ and His Gospel, we can confidently proclaim that Christ is the fulfillment of ancient promise of Genesis 3:15.[131] The true meaning of the zodiac can *only* be understood in and through the revelation of Christ.

Satan has perverted the zodiac through the medium of astrology, ancient and modern. Scripture clearly condemns astrology (II Kings 23:5; Isaiah 47:13–14). The astrology practiced in ancient times is similar to the practice today. Astrology rests upon three basic postulates. First, astrologers believe that the stars influence human affairs. Second, astrologers believe that stars can be used to predict wars, famines, and pestilences. Third, astrologers believe that the fate of individuals can be determined from the position of the stars at their birth. Scripture condemns astrology because it corrupts the real purpose of the star constellations. Christians must shun astrology, but they must also remember that what is perverted has a divine root, a root that is intended to flower into the glories of God.

> *Field of glories! Spacious field,*
> *And worthy of the Master: He whose hand*
> *With hieroglyphics, older than the Nile,*
> *Inscribed the mystic tablet; hung on high*
> *To public gaze, and said, 'Adore, O man!*
> *The finger of thy God.'*

The Federation of Twelve

The order and names of the constellations of the zodiac are most easily remembered by this old poem:

> *The Ram, the Bull, the heavenly Twins,*
> *and next the Crab, the Lion shines,*
> *The Virgin and the Scales;*
> *The Scorpion, Archer and She-Goat,*
> *The Man who carries the Water-pot,*
> *and Fish with glittering tails.*

The key that unlocks the meaning of the zodiac is Genesis 3:15,

> And I will put enmity between you and the woman, and between your seed and her seed; He shall bruise you on the head, and you shall bruise him on the heel.

Adam first heard this cryptic message and the rest of Scripture unfolds its meaning and application. Adam was responsible to name the animals (Genesis 2:19), but God named the stars (Psalm 147:4). Could it be possible that God communicated to Adam the names and meanings of some of the stars? And then, could it be possible that Adam communicated to his children this message so that it might serve as a witness of the promise of Genesis 3:15 to all peoples?

According to some ancient sources (Josephus), it is believed that Abraham, the father of the Hebrew nation, taught the meanings of the stars to the Egyptians.[132] Note that in the Egyptian zodiac, the signs of Leo the Lion and Virgo the Virgin are separated by a Sphinx, a figure with the head of

---

131.   cf. Psalm 2:8; Isaiah 25:7, 42:6–7, 49:8–9, 49:24–25, 60:1–3, 61:1; Daniel 7:13–14; Matthew 12:28–29, 16:18, 28:18–19; Luke 2:32; John 12:31–32; Acts 26:18; Romans 16:20; Colossians 1:13; 2:15; Hebrews 2:14; I John 3:8; Revelation 20:1–3.

132.   Allen, p. 2.

a woman and the body of a lion. The zodiac constellations revolve in a circle around Earth. It is hard to decide where the zodiac begins and ends. It could be possible that the Egyptian division suggests the starting and ending constellations of the zodiac.

The Federation and their Decans

Figure 5–3: Virgo

Figure 5–4: Libra

Virgo:	The figure of a young virgin holding a spike of wheat in one hand and a branch in the other	
Decans:	Coma Berenices, Centaurus, and Boötes	

Libra:	The figure of a pair of balance scales	
Decans:	Crux, Lupus, and Corona Borealis	

Figure 5–5: Scorpio

Figure 5–6: Sagittarius

Scorpio:	The figure of a large, poisonous insect, with its tail lifted up in anger, ready to strike
Decans:	Serpens, Ophiuchus, and Hercules

Sagittarius:	The figure of a centaur (like Centaurus) with a drawn bow and arrow pointed at Scorpio
Decans:	Lyra, Ara, and Draco

Figure 5–7: Capricorn

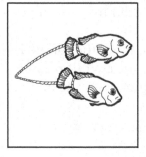

Figure 5–8: Aquarius

Capricorn:	The figure of a goat sinking down as in death, with its hind part ending in the lively tail of a fish
Decans:	Sagitta, Aquila, and Delphinus

Aquarius:	The figure of a man pouring water out of a large water pot
Decans:	Piscis Australis, Pegasus, and Cygnus

Figure 5–9: Pisces

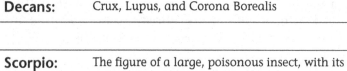

Figure 5–10: Aries

Pisces:	The figure of two large fishes in the act of swimming
Decans:	The Band, Andromeda, and Cepheus

Aries:	The figure of a strong sheep, with powerful curved horns, looking about in a restful and commanding composure
Decans:	Cassiopeia, Cetus, and Perseus

Figure 5–11: Taurus

Taurus:	The figure of the shoulders, neck, head, horns, and front feet of a powerful bull who is moving forward with great energy
Decans:	Orion, Eridanus, and Auriga

Figure 5–12: Gemini

Gemini:	The figure of two humans seated together (NOTE: Some ancient star charts identify these two figures as Adam and Eve.)
Decans:	Lepus, Canis Major, and Canis Minor

Figure 5–13: Cancer

Cancer:	The figure of a crab holding or taking something with its strong pincer claws
Decans:	Ursa Minor, Ursa Major, and Carina (Argo)

Figure 5–14: Leo

Leo:	The figure of a triumphant lion, leaping forth to tear its prey
Decans:	Hydra, Crater, and Corvus

The Zodiac by Season

Winter

Aries

The Egyptians called this constellation Tametouris Ammon, meaning "the reign of Ammon." The Hebrews called it Taleh, meaning "the lamb." The Arabs called it Al Hamal, meaning "sheep, gentle, or merciful." In Akkadian, it is Baraziggar. *Bar* means "altar or sacrifice" and *ziggar* means "right making or righteousness."

Figure 5–15: Aries

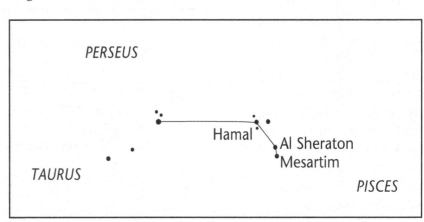

Some individual stars are Hamal[133] (sheep or head)—magnitude of 2.0 at 75 light-years, Al Sheraton (bruised, wounded)—magnitude of 2.65 at 52 light-years, and Mesartim (the bound)—magnitude of 3.9 at 148 light-years. Astronomers suggest that the Sun was in Aries at the time of Christ's crucifixion, the fourteenth day of Nisan. When the judgment of God turned the sky dark, the people of that time could not help but look up and see Aries, the lamb, glittering in the night sky at midday. What a message! The Lamb of God slain for the sins of His people!

As we have seen in Chapter One, Cassiopeia, one of the decans of Aries, could picture the people of God, set up as Christ's bride or queen after being freed from their sins.

---

133. Alpha Arietis is also known as El Nath, meaning "wounded or slain."

Figure 5–16: Perseus

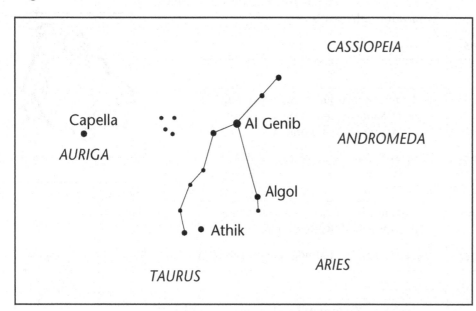

Cetus, the sea monster, was known to the Egyptians as Knem, meaning "subdued." Some stars of this constellation are Menkar (the chained enemy)—magnitude of 2.54 at 130 light-years, Diphda (overthrown or thrust down)—magnitude of 2.04 at 59 light-years, and Mira (the rebel)—variable with magnitude ranging from 2.0 to 10.2 at 130 light-years. This constellation could speak of the defeat of the enemy, Satan.

In Egypt, Perseus was known as Kar Knem, meaning "he who fights and subdues." The Hebrew (Peretz) and Greek (Perses) words both mean "the breaker." Some stars in Perseus are Mirfak[134] (who helps)—magnitude of 1.8 at 522 light-years, Athik (who breaks), Al Oneh (the subdued), and Algol (rolling around)—variable with magnitude ranging from 2.06 to 3.28 at 105 light-years. Perseus is pictured holding a severed head, called Rosh Satan (the head of the adversary) in his hand. Algol is located in that head. This constellation could speak of the victory of Christ breaking Satan's power on behalf of His people.

Taurus

We have seen that Taurus could picture Christ as the Shepherd of His congregated ones. The decans of Taurus complement this message. Orion could picture Christ, the victorious light from heaven who judges all darkness. Auriga could picture Christ, the Good Shepherd, protecting the sheep of His people from the wrath of God (Romans 5:9–10).

In some parts of Florida and Texas, people can see a bright,

Figure 5–17: Eridanus

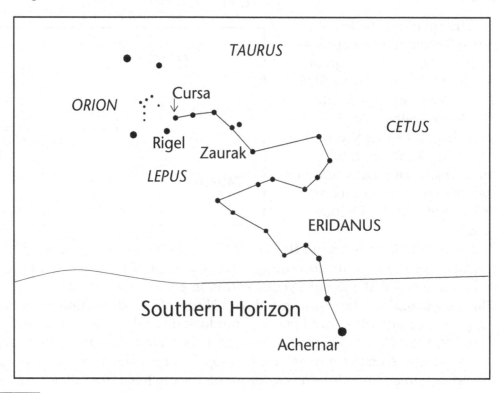

---

134.   Alpha Persei is also known as Al Genib, meaning "who carries away." Some charts identify Al Genib as Gamma Persei.

isolated star low in the southern horizon for a short time in the winter evening. This bluish-white star is called Achernar. With a magnitude of 0.53, it is the ninth brightest star in the sky. Very hot (14,000°K) and 120 light-years distant, its actual diameter is about seven times the size of our Sun and it lies at the southernmost extremity of the constellation Eridanus. Eridanus means "the River of the Judge" and Achernar means "the end of the river." Other bright stars in the Eridanus constellation are Beta Eridani (magnitude 2.79 at 78 light-years), or Cursa (bent down), and Gamma Eridani (magnitude 2.98 at 160 light-years), or Zaurak (flowing). Ancient Greek myths, although perverted, connect this river with fiery judgment. In Scripture, God is often portrayed as "outpouring His wrath" like fire or a stream (Psalm 50:3; Isaiah 30:33, 66:15; II Thessalonians 1:7–8).

Gemini

Gemini pictures union. It could refer to our union with Christ, but, according to its decans, it probably pictures the union of God with man in the person of Christ.

Lepus is pictured as a hare in most constellations. In Egypt, it was pictured as an unclean bird and known as Bashti-beki. *Bashti* means "confounded" and *Beki* means "failing." The Hebrews named it Asedah meaning "to be slain." Another Egyptian name for this constellation was Sura meaning "a lamb." Some individual stars are Arnebo (the enemy of Him that cometh)—magnitude of 2.58 at 900 light-years, Nihal (the mad)—magnitude of 2.81 at 113 light-years, Rakis (bound with a chain), and Sugia (the deceiver). Lepus appears, from the above meanings, to refer to Satan and Christ's victory over him.

As we have seen, the Canis Major and Canis Minor pictures could refer to Christ, the prince of all princes, the exalted Redeemer.

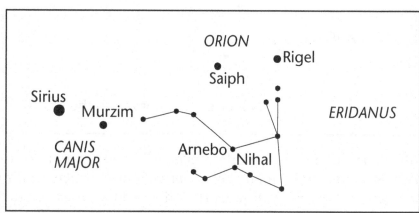

Figure 5–18: Lepus

Spring

Cancer

This constellation was identified by the Egyptians as Scarabaeus meaning "sacred beetle." The Arabs called it Al Sartan, meaning "who holds or binds." The Greeks called it Karkinos, meaning "holding or encircling." The Akkadians called it Sukulra, meaning "the possessor of seed." Cancer is Latin and means "holding."

Some individual stars are Tegmine (holding), Acubene (hiding place or shelter)—

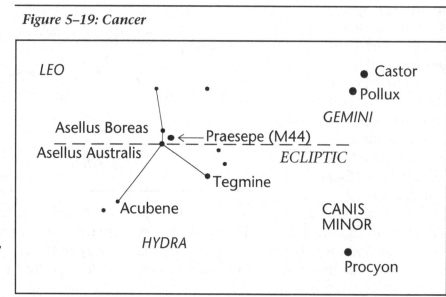

Figure 5–19: Cancer

magnitude of 4.27 at 99 light-years, Ma'alaph (assembled thousands), Al Himarein (the kids or lambs), Asellus Boreas (northern ass)—magnitude of 4.73 at 233 light-years, Asellus Australis (southern ass)—magnitude of 4.17 at 217 light-years, and a beehive cluster (M44) called Praesepe[135] (a multitude, offspring) or Ma'alaph (assembled thousands).

From the above meanings, it appears that Cancer, although it is pictured as a crab, refers to a shelter or keep that protects the people of God from danger. The crab picture may be a perversion. Ursa Minor and Ursa Major continue this theme of protection.

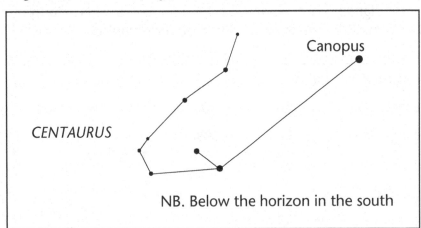

Figure 5–20: Carina (Argo)

Canopus

CENTAURUS

NB. Below the horizon in the south

Carina's most conspicuous star is Canopus, meaning the "possession of Him who cometh." With a magnitude of 0.72, it is the second brightest star in the sky. It is about 110 light-years away and is known as the "Great Star of the South" as it rides along the southern horizon. It is a dazzling yellowish-white star with a temperature of 7,000°K. Other stars in Carina (Argo) are Sephina (multitude), Tureis (the possession), Asmidiska (the released who travel), and Soheil (the desired). Ancient star atlases place Canopus as part of a constellation that pictures a large boat. Argo means "company of travelers." Some ancient civilizations may have associated Noah's ark with this grouping of stars. The ark provided protection and salvation for those who were possessed by it, namely Noah, his family, and the animals. Those possessed by Christ experience that same protection and salvation. In this way Argo continues with the theme established by Cancer, Ursa Minor, and Ursa Major.

Leo

Leo could picture Jesus as the Lion of the tribe of Judah, who goes forth to war treading the enemy under His foot.

Hydra, the serpent, which means "he is abhorred," could picture the enemy being trodden on.[136] Individual stars are Al

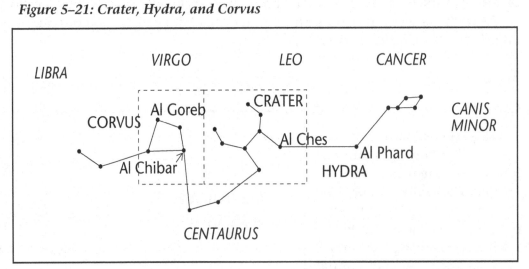

Figure 5–21: Crater, Hydra, and Corvus

LIBRA

VIRGO

LEO

CANCER

CORVUS

Al Goreb

CRATER

CANIS MINOR

Al Ches

Al Chibar

Al Phard

HYDRA

CENTAURUS

Phard (separated, put away)—magnitude of 1.99 at 100 light-years, Al Drian (the abhorred), and Minchar al Sugia (the piercing of the deceiver). Crater, the cup, attached to Hydra, could picture the cup of God's wrath. Corvus, the crow, pecking away at Hydra, could picture birds of prey devouring the enemies of God in judgment (compare with Revelation 19:17–18).

---

135. 515 light-years distant, M44 occupies 1.5° of sky and contains 100 stars.
136. Hydra may be the constellation referred to in Job 26:13. This constellation is used as an example of how God, by His Spirit, adorned (made beautiful) the heavens.

Virgo

Virgo could point to the promise of Isaiah 7:14 and its fulfillment in Matthew 1:23. God, by His Holy Spirit, as a great act of omnipotent power (see Luke 1:35) produced in the Virgin Mary a holy seed. This seed would grow into the promised Branch bringing the blessings of the Kingdom of God to all the nations. Note that Jesus grew up in Nazareth so that the prophets might be fulfilled, "He shall be called a Nazarene" (Matthew 2:23). The root word, Nazar, in Hebrew means "a sprout, shoot, or tiny branch." Isaiah 11:1 speaks of Jesus as a shoot that "will spring from the stem of Jesse" and as a branch (root form of Nazarene) from Jesse's roots that "will bear fruit."

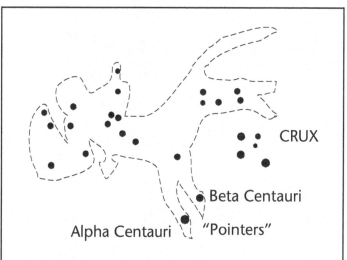

Figure 5–22: Centaurus

The decans of Virgo augment these ideas. As we have already seen, Coma Berenices could speak of the son who is the Desire of all the nations. Boötes continues the theme about the "branch of the Lord."

Parts of the constellation Centaurus can be seen riding the southern horizon. The two brightest stars of Centaurus are Alpha Centauri and Beta Centauri. They are also known as the two pointers in that they "point" the viewer to Crux, the Southern Cross.

Alpha Centauri is the third brightest star in the sky with a magnitude of -0.27. It is yellowish in color with a temperature of 6,000°K. Alpha Centauri is a triple star system. The naked eye sees it as one star. With a telescope, we can see two close bright stars and one faint star 2° away from the bright pair. The faint component (magnitude of 10.7), known as Proxima Centauri, orbits the other two. Navigators around the world know Alpha Centauri as Rigil Kentaurus, the "leg of the Centaur." Its ancient name was Toliman meaning "the heretofore and hereafter." In Scripture, the Lord God is identified as "the Alpha and the Omega, *the* Beginning and *the* End, … who is and who was and who is to come, the Almighty" (Revelation 1:8). Beta Centauri, at a distance of 490 light-years, has a magnitude of 0.66, the tenth brightest star in the sky. Bluish-white, its temperature is about 20,000°K. Also known as Hadar, it is a binary star.

Centaurus, as a constellation, is a picture of a centaur, a being with a twofold nature. In star atlases, it is commonly pictured as a man with the body of a horse. The Hebrews identified this constellation with two names: Bezeh meaning "the despised one" and Asmeath meaning "sin offering." Christ is pictured in Scripture as the despised One who offered Himself for our sins (Isaiah 53). The Greek word for this constellation was *Cheiron* meaning "the one who voluntarily died of a piercing wound." Centaur, the being with a twofold nature, could picture Christ, the God-man, who died on the Cross for our sins.

Summer

Libra

The Hebrews named this constellation Mozanaim, meaning "the scales or weighing." The Arabs named it Al Zubena, meaning "to purchase, to redeem, or to gain." The Egyptians identified it as Lambadia, the "house of propitiation." Propitiation means "to have pity on beforehand; to regain the favor of one previously offended."

Figure 5–23: Libra and Lupus

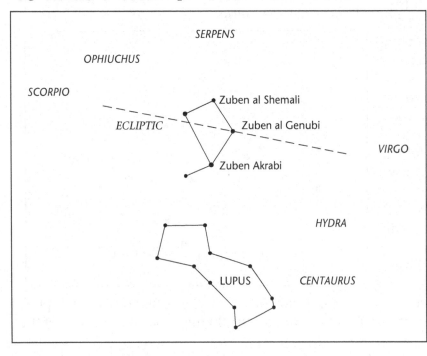

Some individual stars in this constellation are Zuben al Genubi (the price deficient)—a binary at 66 light-years, the brighter has a magnitude of 2.76 and the other 5.15, Zuben al Shemali (the price that covers)—magnitude of 2.61 at 140 light-years, Al Gubi (heaped up high), and Zuben Akrabi (the price of the conflict)—magnitude of 4.02 at 109 light-years.

All men are weighed in the balances of God and found wanting for all have sinned and fallen short of the glory of God (Romans 3:10–23). Into this dilemma came Jesus Christ who covered our sins by paying the price of the conflict, the shedding of His blood (Revelation 5:9). Man's sin has been balanced by the price that covers—Christ's redemption.

Again, the decans of Libra complement this truth. Lupus, the victim, was anciently known as Sura, meaning "sheep or lamb." In Hebrew, it was Asedah meaning "to be slain." In Greek, it was Harpocrates that means "victim of justice." Corona Borealis, as we have seen, points to the Crown bestowed upon the "lamb that was slain."

Most people consider Crux, or the Southern Cross, the most beautiful constellation in the sky. The brightness of its four major stars is greatly enhanced by its elegant and compact arrangement. Today, although you cannot see this constellation from most parts of the Northern Hemisphere, you can see its highest point from parts of Florida and Texas. At the time of Christ, you could see the entire constellation from Jerusalem. *Crux* is Latin for "cross." In Hebrew, its name was Adom, meaning "cutting off." Cutting off is a Hebrew idiom that means death. It is used in Daniel 9:26 about the Messiah being "cut off." Another name in Hebrew was Tau, the last letter of the Hebrew al-

Figure 5–24: Crux

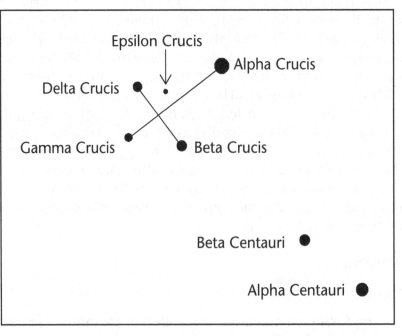

phabet, shaped in a cross, and meaning "mark, limit, or finish." Note that the last words of Jesus on the cross were, "It is finished!" (John 19:30). This constellation could point to the Cross of Christ.

Acrux (Alpha Crucis), binary and bluish-white, is the fourteenth brightest star (magnitude of 0.87) in the sky and lies at a distance of 370 light-years. Beta Crucis, variable and bluish-white, is the twentieth brightest star in the sky (magnitude is 1.28). It is 490 light-years away. Gamma Crucis, our nearest red giant, is the third brightest star in Crux and the twenty-eighth brightest star in the sky (magnitude of 1.64). Its distance is about 230 light-years. Delta Crucis, with a magnitude of 2.82, is another bluish-white star with a computed distance of 570 light-years. Epsilon Crucis is an orange star that is the fifth brightest star in the Crux constellation.

Scorpio

Psalm 91:13, speaking prophetically of Christ, says that He will "tread upon the lion and cobra, the young lion and the serpent you will trample down." This constellation clearly echoes the message of Genesis 3:15. The scorpion, seeking to wound is itself trodden under foot.

We have already seen how two of its decans, Serpens and Ophiuchus, amplify this idea. Serpens, the serpent, is seen struggling with Ophiuchus, the man, who is grasping the serpent.

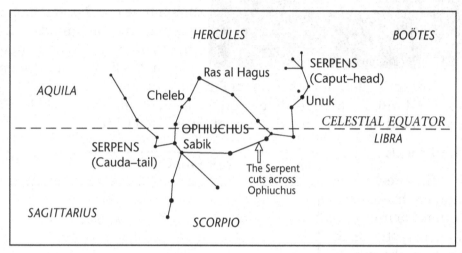

Figure 5–25: Serpens and Ophiuchus

One of the finest globular clusters in the heavens, M5 (magnitude of 6.7), appears in Serpens. M16 (seventh magnitude), a spectacular great nebula containing two strange formations "The Star Queen" and "The Black Pillar," is also found in this constellation.

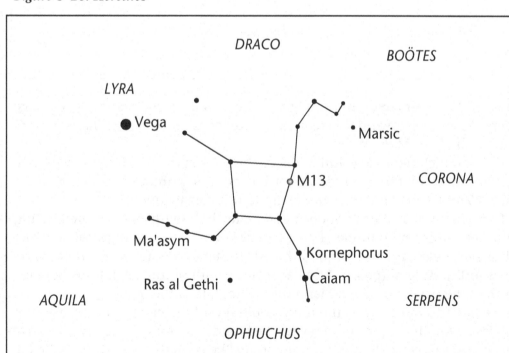

Figure 5–26: Hercules

Two stars in Serpens are Unuk (encompassing)—magnitude of 2.65 at 71 light-years, and Alyah (the accursed)—a binary star at 142 light-years. Some stars in Ophiuchus are Ras al Hagus (the head of him who holds)—magnitude of 2.07 at 60 light-years, Triphas (treading under foot), and Cheleb (serpent enfolding)—magnitude of 2.77 at 124 light-years.

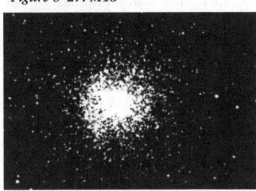

Figure 5–27: M13

The third decan of Scorpio is Hercules. A great globular cluster (M13) is found in Hercules, a celestial wonder that will awe you when you observe it through a telescope.[137] The Egyptians identified this constellation as Bau, meaning "him who cometh." The Arabs named it Al Giscale meaning "the strong one."

Some individual stars are Ras al Gethi (head of him who bruises)—a binary at 410 light-years, the brighter has a magnitude of 3.2 and the other 5.39, Kornephorus (kneeling branch)—magnitude at 2.78 at 103 light-years, Marsic (the wounding), Ma'asym (the sin-offering)—magnitude of 4.48 at 233 light-years, Caiam (treading under foot).

This constellation portrays a mighty man, exalted in his humility, holding up the tokens of victory and with his foot treading upon the head of another constellation, Draco, the dragon. This scene could picture of the triumphs of the exalted Christ.

Sagittarius

The Greeks named this constellation Cheiron, meaning "the chief centaur, the righteous-dealing centaur." The Hebrews called it Kesith, which means "archer." The Arabs identified it as Al Kaus, the arrow. The Egyptians named it Pimacre, meaning "the graciousness, or beauty, of the one coming forth." No other region in the sky so richly possesses such a variety of stars, nebulae, and star clusters. As we look toward this region, we are focusing on the millions of stars in the galactic center, the hub of our Milky Way.

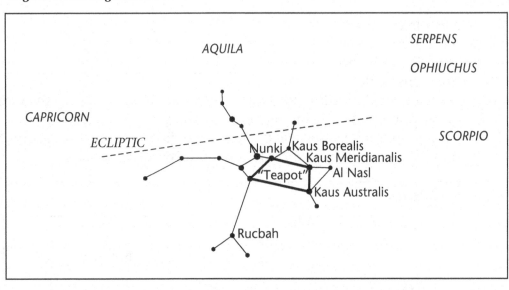

Figure 5–28: Sagittarius

AQUILA

SERPENS

OPHIUCHUS

CAPRICORN

ECLIPTIC

SCORPIO

Nunki   Kaus Borealis
Kaus Meridianalis
"Teapot"   Al Nasl
Kaus Australis

Rucbah

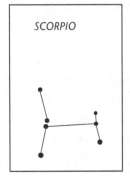

Figure 5–29: Ara

SCORPIO

Christ is pictured in Revelation 6:2 as the rider of the white horse, with bow in hand, crown on the head, riding forth conquering and to conquer. Read Psalm 45 and Psalm 110 in relationship to this constellation.

Some individual stars in Sagittarius are Rucbah (enthroned, seated, riding of the bowman)—magnitude of 4.11 at 250 light-years, Nain (gracious one), Nehushta (the going or sending forth), Al Shaula (the dart), Al Warida (who comes forth), Al Nasl (point), Kaus Australis (south of the bow), Kaus Borealis (north of the bow), and Kaus Meridianalis (middle of the bow).

We have seen that Lyra, the harp, could reveal the victorious ascension of King Jesus. Ara, the altar, could reveal the foundation for this victory. The Egyptians called this constellation Bau, meaning "he cometh." The Arabs called it

---

137. To the naked eye, M13 looks like a fuzzy star. A 4- to 6-inch telescope can resolve some of its stars (brightest of fourteenth magnitude), estimated to total 100,000 or more.

Al Mugamra, meaning "the completing or finishing." The Greeks used Ara in the sense of the cursing of an enemy. This constellation could speak of the Cross of Christ, the place where the enemies of God were cursed and consumed by the fire of God's judgment. Draco continues this theme of an enemy being trodden on.

Autumn

Capricorn

Capricorn is Latin for "goat." The Egyptians called this constellation Hu-penius meaning "the place of sacrifice." The Hebrews called it Gedi, meaning "the kid or cut off" (compare with Daniel 9:26).

The brightest star in Capricorn is Al Gedi, meaning "the kid or cut off." It appears to be a binary, but the stars are unrelated

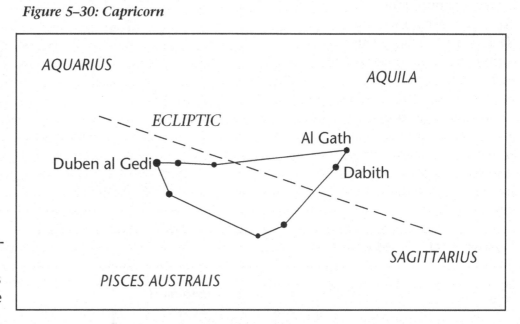

Figure 5–30: Capricorn

gravitationally. One has a magnitude of 4.55 and is 1,100 light-years distant. The other has a magnitude of 3.77 and lies 116 light-years away. The second brightest star in this constellation is Dabih, meaning "the sacrifice slain." It is a binary star at 130 light-years, the brighter has a magnitude of 3.06 and its companion a sixth magnitude star. Deneb al Gedi, meaning "the sacrifice cometh," is a third magnitude star at 50 light-years. This constellation may speak of the ultimate goat of atonement, Christ, slain for our sins. Compare the Old Testament picture in Leviticus 10 and 16 with the goat idea.

Figure 5–31: Sagitta and Delphinus

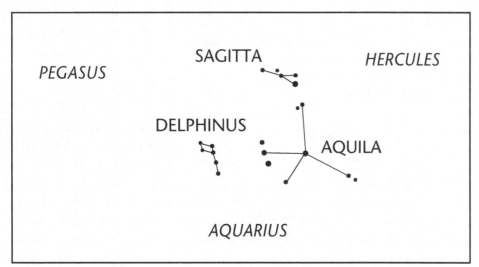

The Hebrews denoted Sagitta, the arrow, as Sham, which means "to destroy or to make desolate." We have already seen that Aquila, the eagle, could picture the sufferings of Christ. The Hebrews denoted Delphinus, the dolphin, as Dalaph (pouring out of water). In Arabic, Dalaph means "coming quickly." The Syriac and Chaldee names of this constellation were Rotaneb or Rotaneu, meaning "swiftly running." The vigorous fish tail of Capricorn could possibly relate to the "aliveness" of Delphinus. Perhaps these two pictures point to the resurrected life of Christ.

Aquarius

This word is Latin for "the water-bearer." In Egypt, it was known as Hupei Tirion, meaning "the place of him coming down or poured forth." The Hebrews named it Deli meaning "water-urn or bucket." The tribal emblem of Reuben, Jacob's firstborn, was the head of a man on a ground of dark red (Numbers 2:10).[138] This man can be linked to Aquarius by the prophecy given to Reuben by his father:

Figure 5–32: Aquarius

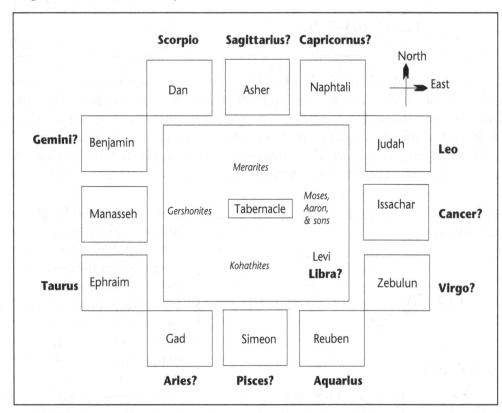

Figure 5–33: The Tribes of Israel

Reuben, you are my firstborn, My might and the beginning of my strength, the excellency of dignity and the excellency of power. Unstable as water, you shall not excel… (Genesis 49:3).

We pause for a moment to review the banner symbols of four of the tribes of Israel. Reuben's banner was a man (Aquarius), Dan an Eagle (Scorpio), Judah a lion (Leo), and Ephraim a bull (Taurus). Aquarius, Scorpio, Leo, and Taurus are the middle signs in the four quarters of the zodiac. Note that these same four figures are found in both Ezekiel and Revelation, representing four living beings, often called cherubim.[139] These living creatures (1) lead in worship around the throne of God (see also Revelation 19:5), (2) chant ceaselessly "Holy, holy, holy," (3) announce God's coming wrath (Revelation 6:1–8), and (4) direct the activity of angels (Revelation 15:7).

---

138.   Edersheim, p. 151.
139.   There is no reason, however, to make an absolute association between the living creatures and the cherubim.

Also from within it *came* the likeness of four living creatures…. As for the likeness of their faces, each of the four had the face of a man; each of the four had the face of a lion on the right side, each of the four had the face of an ox on the left side, and each of the four had the face of an eagle (Ezekiel 1:5, 10).

Around the throne *were* twenty-four elders sitting, clothed in white robes; and they had crowns of gold on their heads. And from the throne proceeded lightnings, thunderings, and voices. Seven lamps of fire *were* burning before the throne, which are the seven Spirits of God. Before the throne *there* was a sea of glass; like crystal. And in the midst of the throne, and around the throne, *were* four living creatures full of eyes in front and back. The first living creature was like a lion [Leo?], the second living creature like a calf [Taurus?], the third living creature had a face like a man [Aquarius?], and the fourth living creature *was* like a flying eagle [Scorpio?]. *The* four living creatures, each having six wings, were full of eyes around and within. And they do not rest day and night saying: "Holy, holy, holy, Lord God Almighty, who was and is and is to come!" (Revelation 4:4–8).

Now when He had taken the scroll, the four living creatures and the twenty-four elders fell down before the Lamb, each having a harp, and golden bowls full of incense, which are the prayers of the saints. And they sang a new song saying, "You are Worthy to take the scroll, and to open its seals; for You were slain, and have redeemed us to God by Your blood out of every tribe and tongue and people and nation, and have made us [or them] kings and priests to our God; and we [or they] shall reign on the earth" (Revelation 5:8–10).

If this association with the zodiac is valid, then John, the author of Revelation, lists them in counterclockwise order—backward around the zodiac. In Revelation 22:1–2, a river of the water of life flows out from the throne of God bringing healing to the nations.

What is God's purpose in linking these constellations with the tribes of Israel? As we have noted in Chapter One, God calls the stars the "host of heaven" (Deuteronomy 4:19). The zodiac constellations surround the Sun, the greater light of our Solar System. God's army of Israel was the earthly "host of the Lord" (Joshua 5:14). When this earthly host fought, "the stars of heaven" also fought with them (Judges 5:20).[140] The twelve tribes of Israel surrounded the tabernacle, the earthly copy of God's heavenly throne. This building housed His shekinah glory, a blazing and almost blinding light.[141] In Genesis 37:9, the sons of Jacob are compared with the

Figure 5–34: The Ark of the Covenant

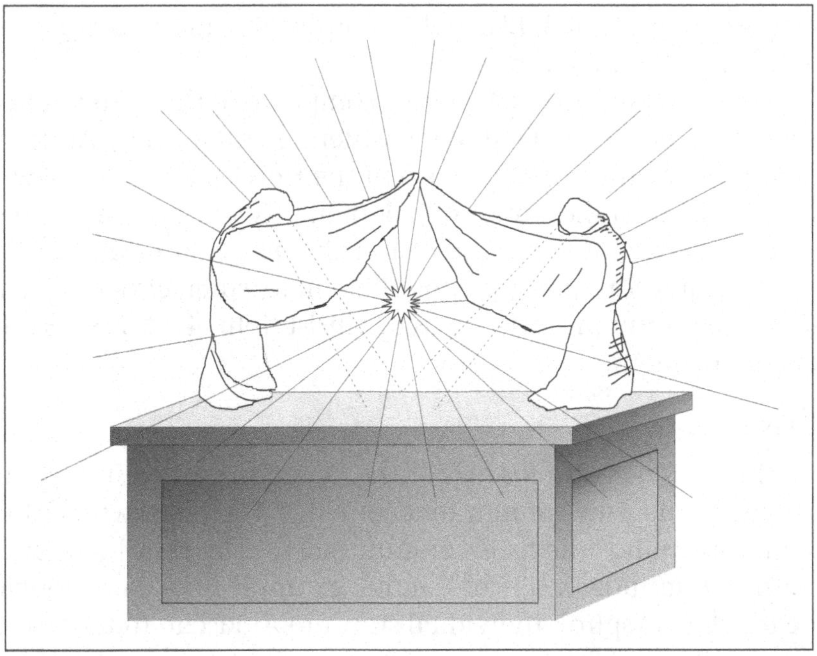

stars. The things of earth pattern the things of heaven. The heavenly host and earthly host are, in God's purpose, somehow connected. When God commanded His earthly army to move, Judah led

---

140. This passage links the earthly host with the heavenly host in battle. When God's people do warfare, they can be assured of God, the divine Warrior from heaven, fighting with them and for them. He will bring His angels to assist the saints in their earthly duties (see Ephesians 6:10–20 and Hebrews 1:13–14).

141. Upon the lid (mercy seat) of the Ark of the Covenant and at its end were the cherubim beaten of gold. The cherubim stood facing each other looking downward to the mercy seat (Exodus 25:20; Deuteronomy 32:11). The shekinah glory of God, a radiant brilliance, hovered over the ark between the cherubim.

the way, Reuben and Ephraim guarded the tabernacle, and Dan formed the rear guard (Numbers 10:13–28). These four tribes led the others in guarding the tabernacle, the repository of God's manifest presence.

Note also that twenty-four elders surround the throne of God in Revelation 4. The context points to these elders as the redeemed church of God consisting of Old and New Covenant believers.[142] The twenty-four elders represent the earthly host of the Lord, seated with Christ the King in the heavenlies, and who manifest His kingly presence on Earth by their obedient praise (Ephesians 2:6; Psalm 22:3). As we have seen, the four living creatures may represent the four quartering tribes of Israel as to their leadership function. These creatures and the twenty-four elders surround the throne of God in worship.

Every time we look at the night sky, we should think on these things. We, believers in the greater Son, the Sun of righteousness, are now the earthly host of the Lord. We surround the throne of God in adoring worship. Our eyes, like the living creatures, perceive His will, knowing what He has done (behind) and will do (ahead). We examine ourselves (within) for out of the heart flow the springs of life (Proverbs 4:23). We move at His orders revitalizing every aspect of life as prophets, priests, and kings. As we do so we take His presence, light, and life with us wherever we go. His light will bring judgment to some, healing to others.

> Now thanks *be* to God who always leads us in triumph in Christ, and through us diffuses the fragrance of His knowledge in every place. For we are to God the fragrance of Christ among those who are being saved and among those who are perishing. To the one *we are* the aroma from death *leading* to death, and to the other the aroma from life *leading* to life (II Corinthians 2:14–16).

Returning to Aquarius, some of its stars are Saad al Melik (the record of the pouring forth)—magnitude of 2.93 at 1,080 light-years, Saad al Suud (who goeth and returneth, or the pourer out)—magnitude of 3.97 at 1,100 light-years, and Scheat (who goeth and returneth)—magnitude of 3.28 at 84 light-years.

Again, the decans of Aquarius complement these meanings. Piscis Australis, the southern fish, is pictured as the recipient of the water poured forth by Aquarius. Pegasus could speak of the coming again of Christ in the person of the Holy Spirit, the One who brings the water of life to us. Or, it could speak of the waters of judgment. Cygnus, the swan, may picture the function of the Holy Spirit in convicting the world concerning judgment (John 16:8–11).

The Aquarian constellations all point to water, either the living water of the Holy Spirit promised to us by Christ (John 4:14, 7:37–39) or the waters of judgment.

Figure 5–35: M74

Pisces

This word is Latin for fishes. The Egyptians called it Pisces Hori, meaning "the fishes of him that cometh." The Hebrews identified it as Dagim meaning "the fishes or multitudes." The spiral galaxy M74 (ninth magnitude) in Pisces is a fine example of a "large looking from the top down" spiral. Individual stars are Al Rischa (band)—a binary at

---

142. Revelation 5:8–10 links the four living creatures with the twenty-four elders. Note that *they* (i.e., both parties) then sing a new song, a song of redemption. Does this mean that the four living creatures are redeemed creatures? The apparent quandary can be resolved by noting that some of the Greek manuscripts (part of the *Majority* text) substitute "them" for "us" and "they" for "we" in verse 10. If this is the correct reading, then this song of redemption may be an antiphonal chorus between the living creatures and the twenty-four elders as follows:
    - Living Creatures, "You are worthy to take the scroll, and to open its seals; for You were slain."
    - Twenty-four elders, "And have redeemed us to God by Your blood out of every tribe and tongue and people and nation."
    - Living Creatures, "And have made them kings and priests to our God; and they shall reign on the earth."

130 light-years, the brighter has a magnitude of 4.3 and the other 5.3, Okda (united), and Al Samaca (upheld).

Figure 5–36: Pisces and the Band

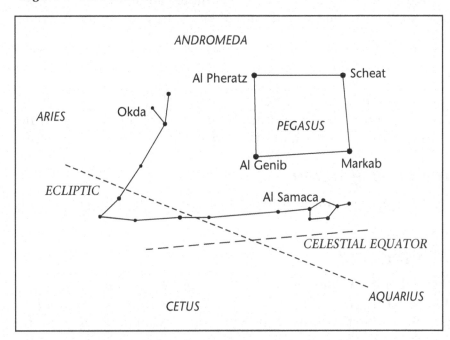

The final decan of Pisces is Cepheus. It speaks of a bruised branch coming to rule. When the people of God suffer, they are encouraged to look to the throne (Revelation 4:1–2). The government of the universe rests in the hands of the sovereign One who has redeemed us in Christ. In Him, we rule as kings on Earth (Romans 5:17).

This constellation may speak of the people of God, united to Him by the power of the Holy Spirit, and upheld by His righteous right hand (see Isaiah 41:8–10).

Attached to each fish is a band that is also connected to Cetus, a decan of Aries. Cetus is a sea monster that probably pictures Satan. The Band could refer the attempt of Satan to bind God's people or the binding of Satan by God's people (Romans 16:20).

Andromeda, as we have already seen, could refer to the sufferings of Christ in and through His people. Triumphant suffering is a part of our conflict with the enemy.

Figure 5–37: Cetus

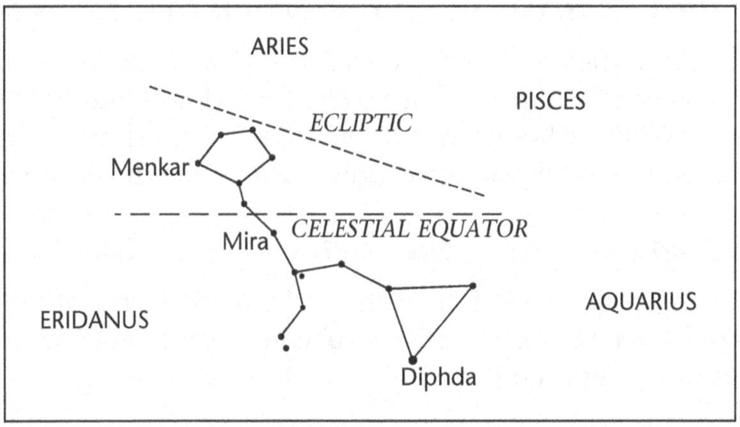

Zodiac Summary

Combining the star-name meanings of each zodiac federation and it associated decans, we can create a summary picture of the person and work of Christ as follows:

Aries—Christ, the Lamb of God

Aries speaks of Christ, the lamb slain from before the foundation of the world. Through His sacrifice, He has chained the enemy, Satan, and broken the bonds that formerly tied His people to slavery in sin.

Taurus—Christ, the Good Shepherd

Taurus pictures Christ as the Shepherd of His sheep, or congregated ones. He protects His sheep by being the light of their pathway judging all darkness.

Gemini—Christ, the God-man

Gemini pictures union, the union of God with man in the person of Christ. In Adam, the first man, all die, but in Christ, the second man, all are made alive. Adam failed God's divine call by obeying the voice of Satan. Christ, by His perfect life and sacrifice, fulfilled His divine call by obeying the voice of His Father. By doing so, Christ, the exalted King of kings, has bound the deceiver with a chain.

Cancer—Christ, the Refuge

Cancer speaks of Christ as a shelter; a refuge that protects the people of God from danger. We are God's people, His possession. The power of God garrisons us. He is to us a refuge from the wind, a shelter from the storm, like streams of water in a desert, like the shade of a rock in a scorched land.

Leo—Christ, the Lion of the Tribe of Judah

Leo portrays Christ as the Lion of the tribe of Judah, who goes forth to war treading the enemy under His foot.

Virgo—Christ, the Branch of the Lord

Virgo points to Christ, the holy seed of the Virgin Mary, the Desire of the nations. Christ is a descendent of King David, son of Jesse. Christ, like a tiny shoot, would grow into the promised Branch and thereby bear fruit by bringing the blessings of the Kingdom of God to all the nations. The "branch of the Lord," God manifest in the flesh, would procure these blessings by dying as the sin offering for all peoples.

Libra—Christ, the Propitiation for Man's Sin

Libra speaks of Christ, a victim of God's righteous wrath, paying the price of man's sin. All men are weighed in the balance scales of God and found guilty before God. Into this dilemma came Jesus Christ, whose blood, as propitiation, covers our sins. As a result of this act of unmerited mercy, Christ has sat down at the right hand of the throne of God crowned with glory and honor.

Scorpio—Christ, the Victor over Satan

Scorpio speaks of the defeat of Satan by Christ at Calvary's Cross. Christ, by his humble death, has been exalted. By faith and obedience, the people of God partake in this victory thereby crushing Satan under their feet.

Sagittarius—Christ, the Archer of God's Judgments

Sagittarius speaks of Christ, full of the beauties of grace and mercy, who shoots the arrows of His word into the hearts of all men. His word is powerful, quick, and sharp. His word is the salvation of His people and the destruction of His enemies.

Capricorn—Christ, the Goat of Atonement

Capricorn speaks of the ultimate goat of atonement, Christ, slain for our sins. After rendering the power of the enemy null and void through His death, He arose victoriously from the grave. He is alive!

Aquarius—Christ, the Water-bearer

Aquarius speaks of Christ, the source of living water for all mankind. If any man is thirsty, he can come to Christ and imbibe the living waters of the Holy Spirit. The Holy Spirit is not only the source of blessings for those who believe in Christ. He also convicts the world of sin, righteousness, and judgment.

Pisces—Christ, the Upholder of God's People

Pisces speaks of the people of God, united to Him by the power of the Holy Spirit, and upheld by His righteous right hand. Christ holds or supports His people in their trials, tribulations, and sufferings in this world. Nothing can separate us from the love of Christ, whether it is tribulation, distress, persecution, famine, nakedness, peril, or sword. In all these things, we are triumphant overcomers, because we are convinced of His steadfast love. His lovingkindness is everlasting.

Responding to God's glory

It is unfortunate so much of what is written on the ennobling subject of astronomy contains no mention of God. Instead of fostering a greater awe and respect of the Creator God, these books reinforce the naturalistic, evolutionist view of the starry host. This is no surprise since the apostle Paul explained many centuries ago:

> For since the creation of the world His invisible attributes, His eternal power and divine nature, have been clearly seen, being understood through what has been made, so that they are without excuse. For even though they knew God, they did not honor Him as God, or give thanks; but they became futile in their speculations, and their foolish heart was darkened (Romans 1:20–21).

In 1836, the publication *The Geography of the Heavens and Class Book of Astronomy* powerfully related the study of astronomy to the Creator of the heavens. Here are a few excerpts from the introduction.

> This department of science [astronomy] unfolds to us the most striking displays of the perfections of the Deity—particularly the grandeur of his Omnipotence. His Wisdom is conspicuously displayed....

> Such subjects and such motions evidently display the omnipotence of the Creator beyond every other scene which creation presents; and, when seriously contemplated, cannot but inspire us with the most lofty and impressive conceptions of the "eternal power" and majesty of Him who sits on the throne of the universe, and by whom all its mighty movements are conducted.

> The study of astronomy has a tendency to moderate the pride of man, and to promote humility. Pride is one of the distinguishing characteristics of puny man, and has been one of the chief causes of all the contentions, wars, devastations, oppressions, systems of slavery, despotisms, and ambitious projects which have desolated and demoralized our sinful world. Yet there is no disposition more incongruous to the character and circumstances of man.

> They [the heavenly bodies] show us what an insignificant being—what a mere atom, indeed, man appears amidst the immensity of creation.

> The moral and religious reflections which the objects of this science naturally suggest, have not been overlooked [in the textbook], and, I trust, will have a tendency to raise the minds of the young to that Almighty Being whose power, wisdom, and superintending providence are so strikingly displayed throughout the regions of the firmament.[143]

For a biblical Christian, a true study of the stars must include a specific emphasis on the meaning of the stars. The word astronomy means "the law of the stars" and it includes the laws that gov-

---

143. Cited in Lester E. Showalter's *Discovering God's Stars* (Crockett, KY: Rod and Staff, 1977), pp. 62–63.

ern the movement, rotations, and regularity of the heavenly lights. Biblical Christian astronomy relates the study of the stars to the revelation of the Bible. This book emphasizes star-name meanings as they relate to the person and work of Jesus Christ. Instead of being an object of worship (like astrology), the stars give eloquent testimony of the glorious purposes of God as centered in the Lord Jesus Christ.

Let us close our study with a response of worship to and adoration of our great and awesome Creator God.

From the *Schlesische Volkslieder*, 1842:

Fair is the Sunshine, fairer still the Moonlight and fair the twinkling, starry host. Jesus shines brighter, Jesus shines purer, than all the angels heaven can boast.

From Stuart K. Hine, 1953:

O Lord, my God! When I in awesome wonder consider all the works Thy hands have made. I see the stars, I hear the rolling thunder, Thy power throughout the universe displayed.

From Thomas Chisholm, 1923:

Summer and winter, and springtime and harvest, Sun, Moon, and stars in their courses above join with all nature in manifold witness to Thy great faithfulness, mercy, and love.

From Henry Van Dyke (1852–1933):

All Thy works with joy surround Thee, earth and heaven reflect Thy rays. Stars and angels sing around Thee, center of unbroken praise. Field and forest, vale and mountain, flowery meadow, flashing sea, chanting bird and flowing fountain, call us to rejoice in Thee.

From Joseph Addison (1672–1719):

The spacious firmament on high, with all the blue ethereal sky, and spangled heavens, a shining frame, their great Original proclaim. The unwearied Sun, from day to day, does his Creator's power display, and publishes to every land the work of an Almighty hand.

Soon as the evening shades prevail, the Moon takes up the wondrous tale, and nightly to the listening Earth repeats the story of her birth; Whilst all the stars that round her burn and all the planets in their turn confirm the tidings as they roll, and spread the truth from pole to pole.

What though in solemn silence all move round this dark terrestrial ball? What though no real voice nor sound amidst their radiant orbs be found? In reason's ear they all rejoice, and utter forth a glorious voice. Forever singing, as they shine, "The hand that made us is divine."

From Amos, the prophet:

Seek the Lord that you may live, Lest He break forth like a fire, O house of Joseph, and it consume with none to quench it for Bethel, you who turn justice into wormwood and cast righteousness down to the earth. He who made the Pleiades and Orion and changes deep darkness into morning, who also darkens day into night, who calls for the waters of the sea and pours them out on the surface of the earth, the Lord is His name (Amos 5:6–8).

Questions for Review and Further Study

Short sentence answers:

Define the following words:

1. Zodiac

2. Astrology

3. Decans

Short essay:

1. What is the relationship between the Ecliptic and the zodiac constellations?

2. What is the relationship between the Ecliptic and the planets?

Long essay:

1. Explain the origins of the practice of astrology.

2. Explain why Scripture condemns the practice of astrology.

3. Compose your own memory aid for the twelve constellations of the zodiac, starting from Virgo and ending with Leo.

4. Answer the following criticisms:

   a. "To say that the meaning of the star names point to the Gospel of Christ is arbitrary and without warrant."

   b. "Christians do not have to prove the veracity of the Gospel by using means (e.g. the Gospel in the Stars" idea) outside of God's written revelation."

5. Find your "astrological sign" based upon your birth date. Derive a presentation of the gospel based on the stars and constellations of your sign. Be ready to use this presentation when someone asks you, "What is your sign?"

   a. Capricorn (22 December – 9 January)

   b. Aquarius (20 January – 18 February)

   c. Pisces (19 February – 20 March)

   d. Aries (21 March – 19 April)

   e. Taurus (20 April – 20 May)

   f. Gemini (21 May – 20 June)

   g. Cancer (21 June – 22 July)

   h. Leo (23 July – 22 August)

   i. Virgo (23 August – 22 September)

   j. Libra (23 September – 22 October)

   k. Scorpio (23 October – 21 November)

   l. Sagittarius (22 November – 21 December)

6. In response to your study of the stars, compose a psalm of praise to God.

Appendix One
The Greek Alphabet

The lowercase letters of the Greek alphabet are used to denote individual stars by constellation, e.g., Beta Ursae Minoris—usually in rough order of brightness, alpha signifying the brightest star in the particular constellation.

α	alpha	ν	nu
β	beta	ξ	xi
γ	gamma	o	omicron
δ	delta	π	pi
ε	epsilon	ρ	rho
ς	zeta	σ	sigma
η	eta	τ	tau
θ	theta	υ	upsilon
ι	iota	φ	phi
κ	kappa	χ	chi
λ	lambda	ψ	psi
μ	mu	ω	omega

Appendix Two

Geometry and the Circumference of Earth

The earliest known measurement of Earth's circumference was made in Egypt by Eratosthenes about 240 B.C. In summary, he based his calculations on (1) the angular height of the Sun and (2) the linear distance between Alexandria and Syene. Note that Eratosthenes had to assume that Earth was round in order to make his calculations.[144]

At noon, during the summer solstice, Eratosthenes observed that the Sun shone down a well at Syene (today known as Aswan) indicating that it was at Syene's zenith. Some 5,000 stades (500 miles) away, he measured a 7.5° angle between the Sun's rays and the obelisk at Alexandria. By assuming that the Sun's rays reaching Earth are parallel and employing simple theorems of Euclidean geometry, he calculated the circumference of Earth as follows:

➢ $\angle O = \angle A$ because corresponding angles formed by the parallel lines l_1 and l_2 and the transversal t are equal.

➢ Since 7.5° is 1/48th of 360°, then the distance from Alexandria to Syene is 1/48th of Earth's circumference.

➢ Therefore, the circumference of Earth equals (48)(500) = 24,000 miles, a remarkably accurate estimate.

Appendices Figure 1: The Method of Eratosthenes

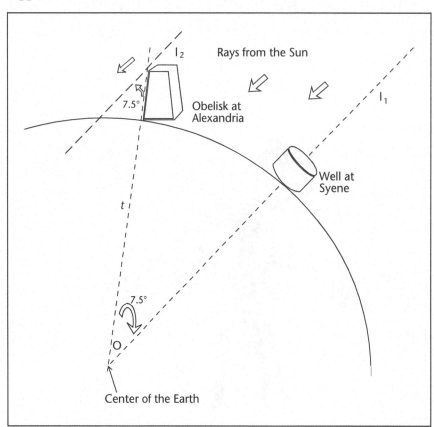

---

144. Of course, the book of Isaiah, written five centuries *before* Eratosthenes, also described the Earth as spherical (Isaiah 40:22).

Appendix Three
Apparent Visual Magnitudes of Celestial Objects

Object	Apparent Magnitude
Sun	-26.50
Full Moon	-12.50
Venus (brightest planet)	-4.00
Sirius (brightest star)	-1.42
Capella	0.06
Rigel	0.14
Beta Centauri	0.66
Acrux	0.87
Beta Crucis	1.28
Uranus	6.00
Neptune	9.00
Pluto	15.00

Appendix Four

Limiting Magnitudes for Various Instruments

Instrument	Faintest Detectable Magnitude
Human eye (city)	3.0
Human eye (country)	6.5
Binoculars[a]	10.0
4 inch (10 cm) telescope	12.0
40 inch (1 m) telescope	17.0
Largest 100 inch (5 m) reflector telescope	24.5

a. Binoculars are good for viewing wide areas of the sky and the Moon. They are usually classified using a pair of numbers, like 7x50. The first number, in this case 7, indicates the magnifying power of the instrument. The letter "x" means "times." The number after the letter "x" represents the diameter of the objective lens (in millimeters). In general, lower powered binoculars have wider fields and higher-powered have narrower fields, which are heavier and thus harder to hold still. Binoculars are often rated in terms of Relative Light Efficiency (RLE). A lower RLE means that the image is less bright. It is calculated by dividing the diameter of the objective lens in millimeters by the square of the power. In a 7x50 pair of binoculars the RLE is 50/7x7 = 1.02. If the RLE is less than 1, the instrument is only good for viewing the Moon. A pair with an RLE of 1 will give you the ability to see objects about 20 times fainter than the unaided eye can detect.

The present limit for any existing telescope is about magnitude 24.5. With this telescope, you can see stars about 16 million (2.512^{18}) times fainter than the faintest stars visible to the unaided eye in open country!

The word *magnitude* comes from the word magnify. *Magnify* means to make great in significance or influence; to create awe.

Truly, as we consider the vast outreaches of space, our desire is to exalt our Creator God.

O magnify the Lord with me, and let us exalt His name together (Psalm 34:3).

The Twenty-Five Brightest Stars

Name	Apparent Magnitude	Constellation	Distance (Light-years)	Luminosity (Sun = 1)
1. Sirius	-1.42	Canis Major	8.7	23
2. Canopus	-0.72	Argo	110	1400
3. Alpha Centauri	-0.27	Centaurus	4.3	1.5
4. Arcturus	-0.06	Boötes	37	115
5. Vega	-0.04	Lyra	27	58
6. Capella	0.06	Auriga	45	90
7. Rigel	0.14	Orion	900	57,000
8. Procyon	0.35	Canis Minor	11.3	6
9. Achernar	0.53	Eridanus	120	650
10. Beta Centauri	0.66	Centaurus	490	10,000
11. Betelgeuse	0.70	Orion	520	7,600–14,000
12. Al Tair	0.77	Aquila	16	9
13. Al Debaran	0.86	Taurus	68	125
14. Alpha Crucis	0.87	Crux	370	3,000
15. Antares	0.92	Scorpio	420	9,000
16. Spica	1.00	Virgo	275	2,300
17. Pollux	1.16	Gemini	35	35
18. Fomalhaut	1.17	Piscis Australis	23	14
19. Deneb	1.26	Cygnus	1,600	60,000
20. Beta Crucis	1.28	Crux	490	5,800
21. Regulus	1.36	Leo	85	160
22. Adhara	1.49	Canis Major	680	9,000
23. Castor	1.59	Gemini	45	36
24. Shaula	1.62	Scorpio	310	1,700
25. Bellatrix	1.64	Orion	470	4,000

a. Luminosity signifies how bright a star is in comparison with the Sun. For example, Bellatrix is 4,000 times brighter, or more luminous, than the Sun.

Appendix Six
Types of Stars

Stars, like our fingerprints, are unique in their composition and color (I Corinthians 15:41). No two stars are exactly alike. Most stars can be divided into a few main classes. Each class is identified by a letter: O, B, A, F, G, K, and M. The color of a star reflects its temperature. Both color and temperature depend upon its chemical composition. The hotter a star is the brighter it shines. From stars of type O to type M, they go from the brightest to the dimmest, from the hottest to the coolest, from the largest to the smallest, and from the heaviest to the lightest.

Type	Color	Temp° K	Stars	Main Chemicals
O	Blue	35,000	Rigel	Helium
B	Blue-white	21,000	Spica Achernar	Helium
A	White	10,000	Al Tair Sirius	Hydrogen
F	Yellow-white	7,500	Canopus Procyon	Calcium
G	Yellow	6,000	Sun Capella	Metals
K	Orange	4,700	Al Debaran	Hydrocarbons
M	Red	3,300	Arcturus Antares	Complex mix

Appendix Seven
Trigonometry and Parallax

If Earth were in motion around the Sun (heliocentricity), then a nearby star would exhibit a parallax (apparent angular shift) with respect to the more distant background stars if observed from two different positions of Earth's orbit. With accurate instruments and the principles of trigonometry, a star's parallax can be determined. Remember, 1 degree (1°) = 60 minutes (60') and 1 minute (1') = 60 seconds (60"). Therefore, 1° = 3600" or 1" = (1/3600)°. A *parsec* (pc) is the distance to a celestial object that exhibits a ***par***allax of one ***sec***ond (1") when viewed from Earth at a right angle to the Sun. One astronomical unit (AU) is the average distance from Earth to the Sun (1 AU = 93,000,000 miles). Using trigonometry, we can calculate the distance, in miles, of one parsec (pc). Let r = 1 pc. Then sin 1" = (1 AU/r). Or, r sin 1"= 1 AU and r = (1 AU/sin 1") = 1.914×10^{13} miles = 206,265 AU. Since light travels at approximately 186,000 miles per second, it travels 5.87×10^{12} miles per year. Therefore, 1 pc = $(1.914 \times 10^{13})/(5.87 \times 10^{12})$ = 3.26 light-years.

Appendices Figure 2: The Parallax Principle

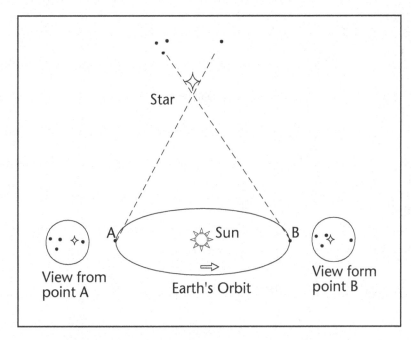

View from point A

Earth's Orbit

View form point B

In the nineteenth century, Friedrich Wilhelm Bessel (1784–1846) measured the parallax of 61 Cygni as 0.29". Remember, 1 pc = 206,265 AU = 1" measured parallax. If a star's parallax is less than 1", then the star is greater than 1 pc away. If a star's parallax is greater than 1", then the star is less than 1 pc away. 61 Cygni's distance, d, is calculated as follows:

d = (1 AU)/sin(0.29") = 711,258 AU = 3.45 pc = 11.25 light-years

This distance method is accurate to 300 light-years. At greater distances, the parallax is too small to be measured reliably. Indirect methods, such as spectroscopic parallax, are used to calculate star distances that are greater than 300 light-years.

The actual determination of parallax, as given in this historical example, is considered by many astronomers to be the principal proof that heliocentricity is the cosmology of our Solar System.

Appendices Figure 3: The Geometry of Parallax

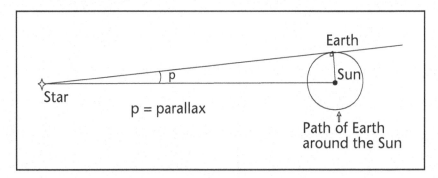

p = parallax

Appendix Eight
Geometry and Latitude

To calculate one's latitude by sighting the Pole star, the observer at P measures the angle between the horizontal at P and the direction of the North Star. Suppose this angle is 30°. The latitude (∠POV) is determined as follows:

Appendices Figure 4: Geometry and Latitude

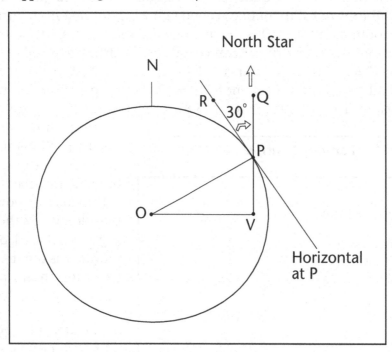

1. Since the horizontal at P is tangent to the circle O, ∠RPO = 90°.

2. Since supplemental angles equal 180°,
   ∠QPR + ∠RPO + ∠VPO = 180° or ∠VPO = 180° – (30° + 90°) = 60°.

3. Since ΔOPV is a right triangle,
   ∠POV (latitude) = 180° – (∠PVO + ∠VPO) = 180° – (90° + 60°) = 30°.

Appendix Nine
Kepler's Laws of Orbital Motion

Appendices Figure 5: Kepler's Laws

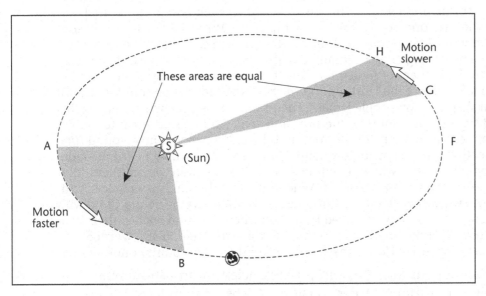

An orbit is defined as the path of one celestial body around another celestial body. There are two types of orbits: open and closed. Open orbits occur when the two bodies are not bound together by gravitational force. When two bodies are bound together by gravity (closed orbits), they revolved around each periodically.

Johannes Kepler (1571–1630), a German astronomer, deduced three laws of closed orbits, called *Kepler's Laws*:

➤ The orbit of a planet traces out the path of an ellipse with the Sun at one of its two foci.

➤ A planet changes its speed according to its distance from the Sun, and the line joining the planet to the Sun sweeps out equal areas in equal times. In the figure, the time that it takes for a planet to travel from one point to the next is the same and the two shaded areas ABS and GSH are equal. This means that a planet moves faster as its orbit brings it closer to the Sun (the nearest point is called the perihelion, point A in the figure), and slower as it moves farther away from the Sun (the farthest point is called the aphelion, point F in the figure).

➤ The square of the time, T, taken by a planet to complete one orbit varies in direct proportion to the cube of its mean distance, D, from the Sun. Mathematically expressed, $T^2 = kD^3$, where k is a constant that is the same for all the planets.

In response to his studies, Kepler often punctuated his writings with psalms of praise to God:

> Great is our Lord and great His virtue and of His wisdom there is no number: praise Him, ye heavens, praise Him, ye Sun, Moon, and planets, use every sense for perceiving, every tongue for declaring your Creator. Praise Him, ye celestial harmonies, praise Him, ye judges of the harmonies uncovered … and thou my soul, praise the Lord thy Creator, as long as I shall be: for out of Him and through Him and in Him are all things…. To Him be praise, honor, and glory, world without end. Amen.[145]

145. Johannes Kepler, "The Harmonies of the World," in *Great Books of the Western World: Ptolemy, Copernicus, Kepler*, edited by R. M. Hutchins (Chicago: Encyclopaedia Britannica, 1952), vol. 16, p. 1085.

Appendix Ten
The "Star" of Bethlehem

The only place in the Bible where this star is mentioned is in Matthew 2:1–12. The text reads:

> Now after Jesus was born in Bethlehem of Judea in the days of Herod the king, behold magi from the East came to Jerusalem, saying, "Where is He who has been born King of the Jews? For we saw His star in the East, and have come to worship Him." When Herod the king heard *this*, he was troubled, and all Jerusalem with him. And when he had gathered all the chief priests and scribes of the people together, he inquired of them where the Christ was to be born. So they said to him, "In Bethlehem of Judea, for thus it is written by the prophet: But you, Bethlehem, land of Judah, are not the least among the rulers of Judah; For out of you shall come a Ruler who will shepherd My people Israel." Then Herod, when he had secretly called the magi, determined from them what time the star appeared. And he sent them to Bethlehem and said, "Go and search carefully for the young Child; and when you have found *Him*, bring back word to me, that I may come and worship Him also." When they heard the king, they departed; and behold, the star which they had seen in the East went before them, til it came and stood over where the young Child was. When they saw the star, they rejoiced with exceeding great joy. And when they had come into the house, they saw the young Child with Mary His mother; and fell down and worshipped Him. And when they had opened their treasures, they presented gifts to Him: gold, frankincense, and myrrh. Then, being warned in a dream that they should not return to Herod, they departed for their own country another way.

Magi, plural of Magus (root of our word "magic"), were ancient court astronomers. They were "from the East"—most likely Zoroastrians, Medes, Persians, Arabs, or even Jews. We do not know their exact number in spite of the suggestion made by the Christmas hymn "We Three Kings." They often traveled from court to court and made special trips to attend the birth or crowning of kings, paying their respects with gifts. For the birth of the King of kings, they brought three gifts:

1. Gold: a kingly gift and most likely used by Joseph and Mary for traveling and accommodation expenses incurred during their stay in Egypt.

2. Frankincense: an ingredient used in the making of incense (Exodus 30:34) that was burned on the altar of incense.

3. Myrrh: a gum resin used as a perfume for embalming and as an ingredient of the holy anointing oil.

The magi's first view of the star was at their local residence. Upon arriving in Jerusalem, they reported that they saw His star rising in the East. The Greek phrase used here, *astera en te anatole*, means "star in the east." Anatole was an ancient astronomical term used to describe when a star rises at Sunset and is visible all night and sets at Sunrise. This is called an acronical rising. While they were in the east (of Jerusalem), they saw His star rise in the east, move across the night sky, and set in the west (toward Jerusalem).

The second time the magi saw the star was at Jerusalem. This time it guided them (went before them and stopped moving—Matthew 2:9) to a specific location in Bethlehem, about five miles south of the holy city. This place was a house (*oikian* in Greek), not the manger, of the child (*paidion* in Greek meaning "a toddler"). This means that they visited Jesus some months after His birth in the manger.[146]

Was this "star rising in the east" an astronomical event like a conjunction? It would seem so since only the magi took note of it (it came as a surprise to Herod). The work of Ernest Martin, au-

---

146. According to Matthew 2:16, Herod ordered the slaughter of male children two years and under as he calculated from the magi. This indicates that Christ was no longer a newborn when the magi visited Him.

thor of the book *The Birth of Christ Recalculated*, will now be used to make some astronomical commentary.[147]

According to Professor Martin, Herod died in the spring of 1 B.C. If this is so, then we need to look at the years 3–2 B.C. to see if some significant conjunctions occurred. The year 2 B.C. was noteworthy in that it marked the 25th anniversary of reign of Caesar Augustus and the 750th anniversary of the founding of Rome. To honor these events, an organized census was taken (see Luke 2:1) to celebrate and gather revenue for these anniversaries.

In Luke 2:8 we note shepherds in fields at night. Farmers would allow sheep to graze the stubble in the fields following harvest. This verse would indicate that Jesus was born in late summer or early autumn.

In the early morning hours of August of 3 B.C., the planets Jupiter and Venus were in conjunction in Leo the lion (near Regulus). Jupiter, in Hebrew *Sedeq*—meaning "righteousness," was the planet that symbolized kingship, coronations, and the birth of kings. The Jews called it the "Planet of the Messiah." Regulus is the brightest star in the constellation Leo, the constellation of kingship. This constellation was the emblem of the tribe of Judah. It was from this tribe that Jesus was to come.

In September of 3 B.C., there was a spectacular conjunction of Jupiter with Regulus. On the eleventh of this month at 2:00 A.M., the kingly planet and the kingly star could be seen in the constellation of the kings rising in the east. Earlier in the evening, at Sunset on the tenth, four celestial bodies could be seen in the constellation Virgo, the Virgin: the Sun, the new Moon (under the feet of Virgo), Mercury, and Venus (see Revelation 12:1 for some remarkable symbolism). These four bodies could also be seen rising in the east at 6:00 A.M. on the eleventh. The magi could not have missed this phenomenon. Could this be the day of Christ's birth? If so, the magi immediately packed their baggage, gathered their gifts, and began their journey to worship the King. As an added note, Sunset on the eleventh was, using the Hebrew calendar, the first day of Tishri, the Feast of Trumpets (see Numbers 29:1 and Leviticus 23:24.).[148]

What about December 25, the traditional date of the birth of Jesus? In the early morning hours of December 25, 2 B.C., Jupiter could be seen in the night sky directly south of Jerusalem standing still (in retrograde motion[149]) at its zenith over Bethlehem. The magi honed in upon this beacon as God continued to guide them on their journey to visit the Christ child. According to Matthew 2:9, the "star" hovered identifiably over a house. I believe, as the magi headed for Bethlehem in the

---

147. Some good astronomy computer software, like the shareware SkyGlobe published by KlassM Software, can be used to "go back in time" and see what was going on in the heavens. We can calculate the occurrence of conjunctions by using the mathematical equations governing the motion of the planets formulated by Johannes Kepler. At the time of Christ, court astronomers could accurately predict these conjunctions centuries in advance of their happening.

148. This was to be a special day of rest for this day heralded a whole month of feasts. The Day of Atonement was celebrated on the tenth day of this month and the Feast of Tabernacles, a seven-day feast, began on the fifteenth day of this month. The first day was a proclamation day. In the morning, Psalm 81 was read as wine was poured over the morning sacrifice in celebration of God's mighty Exodus deliverance and the wilderness wanderings of His people. For the evening sacrifice, Psalm 29 was read in celebration of God's majesty and trumpet-like voice. The trumpets sounded at morning and evening and blew all day. They were: (1) made of silver (redemption money), (2) used for assembling the people so God could speak, (3) blown whenever the people moved during their wilderness wanderings, (4) represented the voice of the King summoning His people to action, and (5) the priests blew the trumpets over the burnt offering to make the people aware of what was happening. For Jesus to be born at this time is significant. He is the trumpet (Revelation 1:10), the ruler of the kings of the earth (Revelation 1:5), and the voice that comes to His people by means of redemption. He is the final voice of God (John 1:1; Hebrews 1:1) and His sacrifice on the Cross is the voice blowing across the burnt offering.

149. A planet normally moves eastward through the stars from night to night and month to month, but regularly exhibits what is called "retrograde motion." Retrograde motion is when a planet, after it passes the opposite point in the sky from the Sun, appears to cease its usual slow eastward movement against the background of the stars; it reaches a stationary point (it stops) and then appears to start moving backwards (westward)—retrograding—against the background of the stars for several weeks. Again, it slows, stops, and resumes its eastward course.

direction of Jupiter, they saw and followed the glory cloud of God, the guiding "fire by night" (see Nehemiah 9:12).

God, who works all things after the counsel of His will (Ephesians 1:11), decreed in His eternal councils that the heavenly bodies would be in such motions during the time of the birth of Jesus Christ the Redeemer. He also arranged the exact date to reflect the fulfillment of one of the ancient feasts of Israel. God conducted, as it were, the orchestra of the movements of the heavens, the prophecies of the Old Testament, the harvest feasts of Israel, and His "glory cloud" in such a manner as to reveal to the magi the time and place of birth of the Messiah, the King of glory.

Appendix Eleven
Precession

Because of a phenomenon known as the precession of the axis, the position of the north pole star changes—imperceptibly during a lifetime—over the centuries. Precession means the gradual shifting of the direction of Earth's axis in space. It is caused chiefly by the pull of the Moon on Earth's equatorial bulge and, to a lesser extent, by the pull of the Sun and planets. The combined effect of these forces is to make Earth's axis perform a circular "wobble" resembling the motion of a "dying top."

Appendices Figure 6: Precession

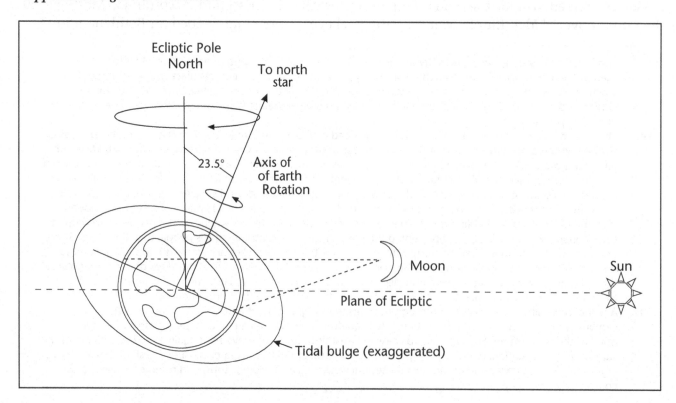

Scientists have calculated, using uniformitarian assumptions,[150] that it takes 25,800 years for the North Celestial Pole to make one complete trip around this circle. The circle has a radius of 23.5° (due to the tilt in Earth's axis). This means that the position of the celestial poles is slowly changing with respect to star constellations. This is why, at the time of Christ, a person in Jerusalem could see the Southern Cross on the southern horizon. During the time of Abraham, the North Star was Thuban in the constellation Draco. Now, Polaris marks the approximate "due north" point in the sky.

Appendices Figure 7: Path of North Celestial Pole

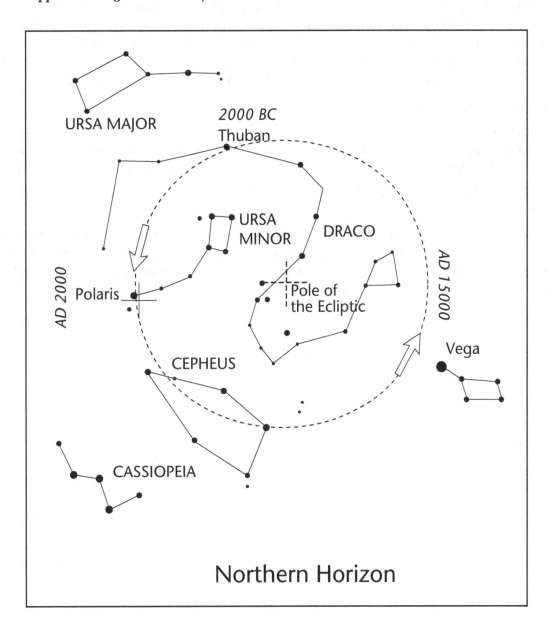

---

150. Uniformitarianism is the belief that the actions of existing physical processes (whether astronomic, biologic, or geologic) are sufficient to account for all past changes and for the present state of the state of things. The principle of uniformity in *present* processes is a valid scientific and Scriptural concept (see Genesis 8:22). Uniformitarianism comes into conflict with biblical revelation when it is used to deny the possibility of *past* (or *future*) suspension or alteration of these processes by the will and purpose of God (see the Genesis Flood as an example).

Appendix Twelve
Cepheids

A Cepheid is a supergiant star that exhibits a regular change in magnitude causing its surface temperature—hence also its Spectral type—to vary. They serve astronomers as a standard for measuring distances in space. This is possible because the length of a Cepheid's period (from maximum to minimum magnitude) is directly proportional to its luminosity. Comparing a star's luminosity with its apparent magnitude enables the astronomer to compute its distance from Earth.

In mathematical terms, let P = period of the pulsation (light variation), then M = average luminosity (i.e., mean absolute magnitude[151]) is determined by the following equation:

1. $M = x + y \log P$ where x and y are measured constants

    To determine the distance, let m = apparent magnitude and r = distance from Earth in parsecs (See Appendix Seven). A *distance modulus formula* that makes use of Isaac Newton's inverse square law (as applied to luminosity)[152] can be developed that expresses the relationship between m, M, and r:

2. $m - M = 5 \log r - 5$

    If two of the three quantities are known, then the other can be determined. Knowing the period (P) of a Cepheid allows an astronomer to determine its absolute magnitude (M). The apparent magnitude[153] (m) is easily measured using spectroscopy. Hence, the distance in parsecs (r) can be calculated using formula 2.

---

151. The brightness a celestial object would appear to have if viewed from a distance of 10 parsecs (1 parsec = 3.26 light-years).
152. The energy per unit area emitted by a given object decreases as the square of the object's distance.
153. The brightness of a celestial object as viewed from the Earth.

Bibliography

Allen, R. H. *Star Names: Their Lore and Meaning.* New York: Dover, 1963 (1899).

Beechick, Ruth. *Adam and His Kin: The Lost History of Their Lives and Times.* Polluck Pines, CA: Arrow Press, 1990.

Berman, Bob. *Secrets of the Night Sky.* New York: HarperCollins, 1996.

Berry, Arthur. *A Short History of Astronomy.* New York: Dover, 1961 (1898).

Bouw, Gerardus D. *Geocentricity.* Cleveland: Association for Biblical Astronomy (Tychonian Society), 1992 (1984).

Brown, Sam. *All About Telescopes.* Barrington, NJ: Edmund Scientific Company, 1975.

Brown, Sam. *Edmund Mag 5 Star Atlas.* Barrington, NJ: Edmund Scientific Company, 1974.

Bullinger, E. W. *The Witness of the Stars.* Grand Rapids: Kregel, 1967 (1893).

Burke, James. *The Pinball Effect.* Boston: Little, Brown and Company, 1996.

Burnham, Robert, Jr. *Burnham's Celestial Handbook.* Three volumes. New York: Dover, 1978.

Chandler, David. *Exploring the Night Sky with Binoculars.* La Verne, CA: David Chandler, 1983.

Chartrand, Mark R. *Skyguide: A Field Guide to the Heavens.* Racine, WI: Western Publishing Company, Inc., 1990 (rev.)

Chilton, David. *Paradise Restored.* Tyler, TX: Reconstruction Press, 1985.

Condos, Teony. *Star Myths of the Greeks and Romans.* Grand Rapids: Phanes Press, 1997.

Culver, Roger B. *Astronomy.* New York: Barnes and Noble, 1979.

Custer, Stewart. *The Stars Speak: Astronomy in the Bible.* Greenville, SC: Bob Jones University Press, 1977.

Deganai, M. H. *Astronomy Made Simple.* Garden City, NY: Doubleday & Company, 1976.

Dickinson, Terence. *Exploring the Night Sky: The Equinox Astronomy Guide for Beginners.* Buffalo, NY: Firefly Books, 1987, 1998.

Dickinson, Terence. *The Edmund Scientific Mag 6 Star Atlas.* Barrington, NJ: Edmund Scientific Company, 1982.

Fleming, Kenneth C. *God's Voice in the Stars: Zodiac Signs and Bible Truth.* Neptune, NJ: Loizeaux Brothers, 1981.

Greenstein, George. *The Symbiotic Universe.* New York: William Morrow and Company, Inc., 1988.

Hislop, Alexander. *The Two Babylons.* New York: Loizeaux Brothers, 1959 (1853).

Humphreys, D. Russell. *Starlight and Time: Solving the Puzzle of Distant Starlight in a Young Universe.* Colorado Springs, CO: Master Books, 1994.

Jaki, Stanley L. *Cosmos and Creator.* Edinburgh: Scottish Academic Press, 1980.

Jordan, James B. "The Geocentricity Question." *The Biblical Educator,* 3:12 (1981).

Jordan, James B. *Through New Eyes: Developing a Biblical View of the World.* Brentwood, TN: Wolgemuth & Hyatt, Publishers, Inc., 1988.

Kolb, Rocky. *Blind Watchers of the Sky.* Reading, MA: Addison-Wesley Publishing Company, 1996.

Levy, David H. *Skywatching.* McMahons Point, New South Wales, Australia: Weldon Owen Pty Limited, 1996.

Maor, Eli. *Trigonometric Delights.* Princeton, NJ: Princeton University Press, 1998.

Martin, Ernest L. *The Birth of Christ Recalculated.* Pasadena, CA: Foundation for Biblical Research, 1980.

Martin, M. E. and Menzel, D. H. *The Friendly Stars.* New York: Dover, 1964 (1907).

Morris, Henry. *Biblical Basis for Modern Science.* Grand Rapids: Baker, 1985.

Morton, J. S. *Science in the Bible.* Chicago: Moody Press, 1978.

Osserman, Robert. *Poetry of the Universe.* New York: Anchor Books, 1995.

Ramo, Chet. *365 Starry Nights.* Columbus, OH: Prentice Hall, 1982.

Rey, H. A. *The Stars: A New Way to See Them.* Boston: Houghton Mifflin Company, 1976.

Rolleston, Frances. *Mazzaroth or The Constellations.* Keswick, England, 1863.

Rucker, Rudy. *The Fourth Dimension.* Boston: Houghton Mifflin Company, 1984.

Schaaf, Fred. *40 Nights to Knowing the Sky,* New York: Henry Holt and Company, 1998.

Schaaf, Fred. *Wonders of the Sky.* New York: Dover, 1983.

Seiss, J. A. *The Gospel in the Stars.* Grand Rapids: Kregel, 1972 (1882).

Showalter, Lester E. *Discovering God's Stars.* Crockett, KY: Rod and Staff, 1977.

Snowden, Sheila. *The Young Astronomer.* Tulsa, OK: EDC Publishing, 1989.

Steidl, Paul M. *The Earth, the Stars, and the Bible.* Phillipsburg, PA: Presbyterian and Reformed Publishing Company, 1979.

Tenant, Catherine. *The Box of Stars: A Practical Guide to the Night Sky and to its Myths and Legends.* New York: Bulfinch Press, 1993.

van der Kamp, Walter. *The Cosmos, Einstein and Truth.* Victoria, British Columbia: Walter van der Kamp, 1993.

Warner, Lionel. *Stars and Planets of the Southern Hemisphere.* Sydney, New South Wales, Australia: A. H. & A. W. Reed, Ltd., 1978.

Wilson, Douglas, ed. *The Forgotten Heavens.* Moscow, ID: Canon Press, 1989.

Woodrow, Ralph. *Babylon Mystery Religion.* Riverside, CA: Ralph Woodrow Evangelistic Association, 1981.

Star-Name Glossary and Pronunciation Guide

Sequenced by constellation and star magnitude[154]

Andromeda

an-DROH-me-duh: set up as queen, the chained, the afflicted, the weak

Al Pheratz
al-FEE-rats, Sirrah (Alpha Andromedae): the broken down

Mirach
MY-rack (Beta Andromedae): the weak

Al Maach
al-MAK (Gamma Andromedae): the struck down

Aquarius

ah-KWAIR-ee-us: the place of him coming down, poured forth, water bearer, water bucket

Saad al Melik
sa-ad-al-ME-lick (Alpha Aquarii): the record of the pouring forth

Saad al Suud
sa-ad-al-SU-ud (Beta Aquarii): the pourer out

Scheat
SHEE-at, Skat (Delta Aquarii): who goeth and returneth

Aquila

uh-KWI-luh: eagle

Al Tair
al-TAIR (Alpha Aquilae): the wounding

Al Shain
al-SHANE (Beta Aquilae): the bright; scarlet covered

Tarazed
TAR-uh-zed (Gamma Aquilae): wounded, torn

Al Cair
al-CARE, Denebokab (Delta Aquilae): the piercing

Al Okal
al-OK-al (Epsilon Aquilae): wounded in the heel

Ara

AR-uh: he cometh, the completing or finishing, altar

Aries

AIR-eez: the lamb, sheep, gentle, merciful, sacrifice, righteousness

Al Hamal, El Nath (Alpha Arietis)
head, sheep

Al Sheraton
al-SHAIR-uh-tan (Beta Arietis): bruised, wounded

Mesartim
meh-sar-TIM (Gamma Arietis): the bound

Auriga

oh-RYE-gah: shepherd

Capella
kah-PELL-uh, Alioth (Alpha Aurigae): she goat

Menkalinan
men-KAL-ih-nan (Beta Aurigae): chain of the goats

Boötes

boh-OH-teez: the one who rules, the coming one

Arcturus
ark-TOO-rus (Alpha Boötis): he cometh

Nekkar
NECK-ker (Beta Boötis): pierced

Mirac, Mizr, Mizar
MY-zar (Epsilon Boötis): the coming forth as an arrow, preserving, guarding

Muphride, Muphrid, Mufrid
MU-frid (Eta Boötis): who separates

Al Kalurops
al-kal-YOU-rops (Mu Boötis): the branch, treading under foot

Cancer

CAN-ser: who holds or binds, encircling, possessor of the seed; rest secured

Acubene
ah-cue-bin-EH, Acubens (Alpha Cancri): hiding place or shelter

Asellus Boreas
ah-SELL-us bor-ee-ASS (Gamma Cancri): northern ass

Asellus Australis
ah-SELL-us os-TRAH-lis (Delta Cancri): southern ass

Tegmine
TEG-mine (Zeta Cancri): holding

---

154. The *Edmund Mag 5 Star Atlas* is the source for determining the pronunciation of most of the star names. Note that pronunciations will vary according to cultural and/or national dialects. In some cases, a star may have more than one name assigned to it or one name may designate more than one star. The ancient (Hebrew or Noetic*) roots from which they were formed largely determines the meanings of these names. In some cases, modern meanings are also listed (e.g., Regulus, Antares). Based upon which lexicon and/or philological authority is used, variations in meaning are possible. In some cases, the scientific name of the star (e.g., Gamma Andromedae—NOTE: *Andromedae* is the genitive form of the constellation name) is not certain and this is indicated by a question mark (?). *The word *noetic* means "of, pertaining to, or originating in the mind."

Al Himarein
> al-HYMN-ar-ene (? Cancri): kids or lambs

Praesepe
> PRAY-seh-pea; "beehive" cluster (M44 in Cancer), Ma'alaph: a multitude, offspring

Canis Major (greater)

KAH-niss MAY-jer: head, leader, coming quickly, wolf, hawk, dog

Sirius
> SEER-ee-us (Alpha Canis Majoris): prince, leader of heaven, chief of the host, sparkling one, scorching, dog star

Murzim, Mirzam
> MURR-zam (Beta Canis Majoris): prince or ruler

Wesen
> WESS-en (Delta Canis Majoris): the bright, the shining

Adhara
> add-DARE-rah (Epsilon Canis Majoris): the glorious

Canis Minor (lesser)

KAH-nis MY-ner: conqueror, victorious

Procyon
> PRO-see-on (Alpha Canis Minoris): redeemer, rising before the dog

Al Gomeisa
> al-go-MAY-sah (Beta Canis Minoris): the burdened, loaded, bearing

Al Gomeyra
> al-go-MAY-rah (? Canis Minoris): who completes or perfects

Al Shira
> al-SHY-rah (? Canis Minoris): prince or chief of left hand

Capricorn

kap-reh-KORN: the place of sacrifice, cut off, goat

Al Gedi
> al-JED-eye (Alpha Capricorni): cut off

Dabih
> DAB-eh (Beta Capricorni): the sacrifice slain

Deneb al Gedi
> DEN-ebb al-JED-eye (Delta Capricorni): the sacrifice cometh

Carina (Argo)

ka-RYE-nah (Argo—AR-go): company of travelers

Canopus
> can-OH-puss (Alpha Carinae): the possession of him who cometh

Tureis
> TUR-ace (Iota Carinae): possession in hand

Asmidiska
> as-meh-DISK-ah (? Carinae): the released who travel

Soheil
> so-HEIL (? Carinae): the desired

Sephina
> sef-HEE-nah (? Carinae): multitude

Cassiopeia

kass-ee-oh-PEE-uh: the freed, set up as a queen, enthroned

Schedir
> SHED-durr (Alpha Cassiopei): the freed

Caph
> kaff (Beta Cassiopei): the branch

Ruchbah
> RUK-bah (Delta Cassiopei): the enthroned, the seated

Centaurus

sen-TOR-us: the despised one, sin offering; the one voluntarily dying of a piercing wound

Rigil Kentaurus
> RYE-jill ken-TOR-us, Toliman—TOLL-eh-man (Alpha Centauri): leg of the Centaur, the heretofore and hereafter

Hadar
> HAD-ar, Agena—ah-JEN-ah (Beta Centauri): knee of the Centaur

Cepheus

SEE-fee-us: this one cometh to rule, the branch

Al Deramin
> al-DARE-uh-min (Alpha Cephei): coming quickly

Al Phirk
> al-FIRK, Alfirk (Beta Cephei): the redeemer

Al Rai
> al-RYE, Errai (Gamma Cephei): who bruises or breaks

Cetus

SEE-tus: subdued

Menkar
> MEN-kar (Alpha Ceti): the chained enemy

Diphda
> DIP-dah (Beta Ceti): overthrown or thrust down

Mira
> MY-ruh (Omicron Ceti): the rebel

Coma Berenices

KOH-mah bear-eh-NEE-seez: the desired one

Corona Borealis
> kor-OH-nah bor-ee-AL-is: royal crown, jewel, northern crown

Al Phecca
> al-FECK-uh (Alpha Coronae Borealis): the shining

Corvus

KOR-vus: the breaking of the enemy

Al Chiba
> al-CHEH-bah (Alpha Corvi): the curse inflicted

Al Goreb
> al-GOR-eb, Gienah (Gamma Corvi): the raven

Mincher al Goreb

MIN-cher al-GOR-eb (Delta Corvi): the raven tearing to pieces

Crater

KRAY-ter: cup of wrath

Crux

kruks: cross, cutting off

Cygnus

SIG-nus: swan

Deneb

DEN-ebb (Alpha Cygni): this from afar, the judge

Al Bireo

al-BURR-ee-oh (Beta Cygni): flying quickly

Sadr

SAD-der (Gamma Cygni): who returns as in a circle

Azel/Fafage

ah-ZEL/fa-FAGE (Pi Cygni): who goes and returns quickly; gloriously shining forth

Delphinus

del-FIE-nus: coming quickly, swiftly running

Draco

DRAY-koh: trodden on, the serpent accursed, the head of the subtle who is to be destroyed

Thuban

THEW-ban (Alpha Draconis): the subtle

Eridanus

eh-RID-an-us: river of the judge

Achernar

AKE-er-nar (Alpha Eridani): the end of the river

Cursa

CUR-sa (Beta Eridani): bent down

Zaurak

ZAW-rack, Zurak (Gamma Eridani): flowing

Gemini

JEM-eh-nye: the place of him who cometh, the united

Castor

CASS-ter (Alpha Geminorum): ruler, judge

Pollux

POLL-lux (Beta Geminorum): who cometh to suffer

Al Hena

al-HEN-uh (Gamma Geminorum): to wound or afflict

Wasat

WAY-sat (Delta Geminorum): set

Mebsuta

meb-SUE-tah (Epsilon Geminorum): treading under foot

Propus

PRO-pus (Eta Geminorum): the branch

Al Dira

al-DYE-rah (? Geminorum): the seed or branch

Al Giauza

al-gi-AWE-zah (? Geminorum): the palm branch

Hercules

HER-kyu-leez: him who cometh, the strong one

Ras al Gethi

rahs-al-GETH-ee (Alpha Herculis): head of him who bruises

Kornephorus

KOR-ne-for-us (Beta Herculis): kneeling branch

Caiam

KEYE-am, Gwam (Gamma Herculis): treading under foot

Ma'asym

ma-ASS-em (Lambda Herculis): the sin-offering

Marsic

MAR-sik (Chi Herculis): the wounding

Hydra

HY-dra: serpent, he is abhorred

Al Phard

AL-fard (Alpha Hydrae): separated, put away

Al Drian

al-DRY-an (? Hydrae): the abhorred

Minchar al Sugia

min-KAR-al-SUG-eh-ah (? Hydrae): the piercing of the deceiver

Leo

LEE-oh: pouring out, hunting down its prey, the rending lion

Regulus

REG-you-luss (Alpha Leonis): treading under foot, little king

Denebola

deh-NEB-oh-la (Beta Leonis): the judge who cometh

Al Geiba

al-JEE-buh (Gamma Leonis): the exaltation

Zozma

ZOZ-mah (Delta Leonis): shining forth

Lepus

LEE-pus: confounded, failing, to be slain, lamb

Arnebo

ARE-nego (Alpha Leporis): the enemy of him that cometh

Nihal

neh-HAL (Beta Leporis): the mad

Rakis

RAH-kis (? Leporis): bound with a chain

Sugia

SUE-gee-ah (? Leporis): the deceiver

Libra

LEE-bra: the scales or weighing, to purchase, redeem, or to gain, the house of propitiation

Zuben al Genubi

zoo-ben-ell-jen-NEW-bee (Alpha Librae): the price deficient

Zuben al Shemali

    zoo-ben-ess-sha-MAY-lee (Beta Librae): the price that covers

Zuben Akrabi

    zoo-ben-ack-RAH-bee (Gamma Librae): the price of the conflict

Al Gubi

    al-GOO-bee (Eta [?] Librae): heaped up high

Lupus

LOO-pus: sheep, lamb, victim, to be slain, victim of justice

Lyra

LYE-rah: the serpent ruled, harp

Vega

    VEE-guh (Alpha Lyrae): exaltation, triumph, victory

Sheliak

    SHE-leh-ak (Beta Lyrae): eagle

Sulaphat

    su-LAH-fat (Gamma Lyrae): springing up, ascending

Ophiuchus

oh-fee-U-cuss: holding the serpent

Ras al Hagus

    RAS-el-haig-uss (Alpha Ophiuchi): the head of him who holds

Cheleb

    CHAY-leb (Beta Ophiuchi): serpent enfolding

Triphas

    TREYE-fas (? Ophiuchi): treading under foot

Orion

oh-RYE-un: he who triumphs, the light of heaven, the strong one, the giant

Betelgeuse

    BETT-el-jews or BETT-ed-juzz (Alpha Orionis): the coming of the branch

Rigel

    RYE-jell (Beta Orionis): the foot that crushes

Bellatrix

    bell-LAY-trix (Gamma Orionis): quickly coming to swiftly destroy

Al Mintakah

    al-min-TAK-uh (Delta Orionis): the belt

Al Nilam

    al-nih-LAM (Epsilon Orionis): string of pearls

Al Nitak

    al-nih-TAK (Zeta Orionis): the wounded one

Na'ir al Saiph

    nay-er-al-SAFE (Iota Orionis): brightly bruised

Saiph

    safe (Kappa Orionis): bruised

Pegasus

PEG-a-sus: chief ("pega") horse ("sus" can also mean "swiftly coming"), the horse of the gushing fountain

Markab

    MAR-kab (Alpha Pegasi): returning from afar

Scheat

    SHEE-at (Beta Pegasi): who goeth and returneth

Al Genib

    al-JEE-nib (Gamma Pegasi): who carries away

Enif

    ENN-if (Epsilon Pegasi): nose, the water

Matar

    MAH-tar (Eta Pegasi): who causes to overflow; fortunate rain

Perseus

PURR-see-us: he who fights and subdues, the breaker

Mirfak

    MURR-fak (Alpha Persei) or Al Genib—al-JEE-nib (Gamma Persei): who helps or who carries away

Algol

    AL-gol (Beta Persei): rolling around

Athik

    ah-THICK (Omicron Persei): who breaks

Al Oneh

    al-ON-eh (? Persei): the subdued

Pisces

PIE-seez: the fishes of him that cometh, multitudes

Al Rischa

    al-RISH-ah (Alpha Piscium): band

Al Samaca

    al-sah-MACK-ah (Theta Piscium): upheld

Okda

    AWK-dah (Phi Piscium): united

Piscis Australis

PIE-sis os-TRAH-lis: stream, southern fish

Fomalhaut

    FOAM-al-ought (Alpha Piscis Austrini): mouth of the fish

Sagitta

sa-JIT-ah: to destroy or make desolate, arrow

Sagittarius

sadge-ih-TAIR-ee-us: archer, arrow, the beauty of the one coming forth

Rucbah

    RUK-bah, Rukbat (Alpha Sagittarii): the enthroned, the seated, riding of the bowman

Al Nasl

    al-NAS-el (Gamma Sagittarii): point

Kaus Meridianalis

    KOSS oss-TRAY-liss (Delta Sagittarii): middle of the bow

Kaus Australis

    KOSS os-TRAH-lis (Epsilon Sagittarii): south of the bow

Al Shaula

    al-SHAW-lah, Ascella (Zeta Sagittarii): the dart

Kaus Borealis
> KOSS bor-ee-AL-is (Lambda Sagittarii): north of the bow

Al Warida
> al-WAR-eye-dah (? Sagittarii): who comes forth

Nain
> nayn (? Sagittarii): gracious one

Nehushta
> NEH-ush-tah (? Sagittarii): the going or sending forth

Scorpio, Scorpius
SKOR-pee-oh/us: conflict or war, the attack of the enemy, wounding him who cometh

Antares
> an-TAIR-ees (Alpha Scorpii): wounding, rival of Mars

Lesath
> LEA-sath (Upsilon Scorpii): perverse

Serpens
SIR-penz: serpent

Unuk
> YOU-nuk (Alpha Serpentis): encompassing

Alyah
> AL-yah (Theta Serpentis): the accursed

Taurus
TORR-us: who saves or delivers, head, chief, exaltation, high place, coming, ruling

Aldebaran
> al-DEB-uh-ran (Alpha Tauri): the follower, bright one of the follower

El Nath
> el-NATH (Beta Tauri): wounded, slain

Alcyone
> al-SIGH-oh-nee (Eta Tauri): the center

Pleiades
> PLEE-uh-deez cluster (in Taurus): gathering, the congregation of the judge or ruler, seven sisters

Hyades
> HY-uh-deez cluster (in Taurus): congregated

Ursa Major (greater)
ER-suh MAY-jer: the assembled together

Dubhe
> DUBB-be (Alpha Ursae Majoris): flock

Merach, Merak
> ME-rack (Beta Ursae Majoris): purchased flock

Phaeda, Phacda
> FECK-dah (Gamma Ursae Majoris): visited, guarded, numbered

Megrez
> MEH-grez (Delta Ursae Majoris): tail

Alioth
> ALLEY-oth (Epsilon Ursae Majoris): she goat

Mizar
> MY-zar (Zeta Ursae Majoris): separate or small

Benet Naish
> be-net-NASH, Alkaid al-KAID (Eta Ursae Majoris): the daughters of the assembly or the assembled

Al Cor
> al-KOR (g, 80 Ursae Majoris): the lamb

Ursa Minor (lesser)
ER-suh MY-ner: fold, rest, security

Polaris
> pole-AIR-iss, Al Ruccaba (Alpha Ursae Minoris): turned or ridden on

Kochab
> KOE-kab (Beta Ursae Minoris): waiting him who cometh

Al Pherkadain
> al-FUR-kad-aine, Pherkad FUR-kad (Gamma Ursae Minoris): the redeemed assembly

Virgo
VER-go: virgin, branch

Spica
> SPY-kay, Al Zimach, Tsemech (Alpha Virginis): the branch, ear of corn
> Zavijaveh (Beta Virginis): the gloriously beautiful

Al Mureddin
> al-NUR-eh-din, Vindemiatrix—vin-dee-MY-uh-trix (Epsilon Virginis): who shall come down, who shall have dominion, the son, branch, who cometh

---

Whirlpool Galaxy

Sequenced by Star/Star Cluster

Achernar
AKE-er-nar (Alpha Eridani): the end of the river

Acubene
ah-cue-bin-EH, Acubens (Alpha Cancri): hiding place or shelter

Adhara
add-DARE-rah (Epsilon Canis Majoris): the glorious

Al Bireo
al-BURR-ee-oh (Beta Cygni): flying quickly

Al Cair
al-CARE, Denebokab (Delta Aquilae): the piercing

Al Chiba
al-CHEH-bah (Alpha Corvi): the curse inflicted

Al Cor
al-KOR (g, 80 Ursae Majoris): the lamb

Al Deramin
al-DARE-uh-min (Alpha Cephei): coming quickly

Al Dira
al-DYE-rah (? Geminorum): the seed or branch

Al Drian
al-DRY-an (? Hydrae): the abhorred

Al Gedi
al-JED-eye (Alpha Capricorni): cut off

Al Geiba
al-JEE-buh (Gamma Leonis): the exaltation

Al Genib
al-JEE-nib (Gamma Persei): who carries away

Al Genib
al-JEE-nib (Alpha Pegasi): who carries away

Al Giauza
al-gi-AWE-zah (? Geminorum): the palm branch

Al Gomeisa
al-go-MAY-sah (Beta Canis Minoris): the burdened, loaded, bearing

Al Gomeyra
al-go-MAY-rah (? Canis Minoris): who completes or perfects

Al Goreb
al-GOR-eb, Gienah (Gamma Corvi): the raven

Al Gubi
al-GOO-bee (Eta [?] Librae): heaped up high

Al Hama
El Nath (Alpha Arietis): head, sheep

Al Hena
al-HEN-uh (Gamma Geminorum): to wound or afflict

Al Himarein
al-HYMN-ar-ene (? Cancri): kids or lambs

Al Kalurops
al-kal-YOU-rops (Mu Boötes): the branch, treading under foot

Al Maach
al-MAK (Gamma Andromedae): the struck down

Al Mintakah
al-min-TAK-uh (Delta Orionis): the belt

Al Mureddin
al-NUR-eh-din, Vindemiatrix—vin-dee-MY-uh-trix (Epsilon Virginis): who shall come down, who shall have dominion, the son, branch, who cometh

Al Nasl
al-NAS-el (Gamma Sagittarii): point

Al Nilam
al-nih-LAM (Epsilon Orionis): string of pearls

Al Nitak
al-nih-TAK (Zeta Orionis): the wounded one

Al Okal
al-OK-al (Epsilon Aquilae): wounded in the heel

Al Oneh
al-ON-eh (? Persei): the subdued

Al Phard
AL-fard (Alpha Hydrae): separated, put away

Al Phecca
al-FECK-uh (Alpha Coronae Borealis): the shining

Al Pheratz
al-FEE-rats, Sirrah (Alpha Andromedae): the broken down

Al Pherkadain
al-FUR-kad-aine, Pherkad—FUR-kad (Gamma Ursae Minoris): the redeemed assembly

Al Phirk
al-FIRK, Alfirk (Beta Cephei): the redeemer

Al Rai
al-RYE, Errai (Gamma Cephei): who bruises or breaks

Al Rischa
al-RISH-ah (Alpha Piscium): band

Al Samaca
al-sah-MACK-ah (Theta Piscium): upheld

Al Shain
al-SHANE (Beta Aquilae): the bright; scarlet covered

Al Shaula
al-SHAW-lah, Ascella (Zeta Sagittarii): the dart

Al Sheraton

al-SHAIR-uh-tan (Beta Arietis): bruised, wound-ed

Al Shira

al-SHY-rah (? Canis Minoris): prince or chief of left hand

Al Tair

al-TAIR (Alpha Aquilae): the wounding

Al Warida

al-WAR-eye-dah (? Sagittarii): who comes forth

Alcyone

al-SIGH-oh-nee (Eta Tauri): the center

Aldebaran

al-DEB-uh-ran (Alpha Tauri): the follower, bright one of the follower

Algol

AL-gol (Beta Persei): rolling around

Alioth

ALLEY-oth (Epsilon Ursae Majoris): she goat

Alyah

AL-yah (Theta Serpentis): the accursed

Antares

an-TAIR-ees (Alpha Scorpii): wounding, rival of Mars

Arcturus

ark-TOO-rus (Alpha Boötes): he cometh

Arnebo

ARE-nego (Alpha Leporis): the enemy of him that cometh

Asellus Australis

ah-SELL-us os-TRAH-lis (Delta Cancri): southern ass

Asellus Boreas

ah-SELL-us bor-ee-ASS (Gamma Cancri): north-ern ass

Asmidiska

as-meh-DISK-ah (? Carinae): the released who travel

Athik

ah-THICK (Omicron Persei): who breaks

Azel/Fafage

ah-ZEL/fa-FAGE (Pi Cygni): who goes and re-turns quickly; gloriously shining forth

Bellatrix

bell-LAY-trix (Gamma Orionis): quickly coming to swiftly destroy

Benet Naish

be-net-NASH, Alkaid al-KAID (Eta Ursae Ma-joris): the daughters of the assembly or the as-sembled

Betelgeuse

BETT-el-jews or BETT-ed-juzz (Alpha Orionis): the coming of the branch

Caiam

KEYE-am, Gwam (Gamma Herculis): treading under foot

Canopus

can-OH-puss (Alpha Carinae): the possession of him who cometh

Capella

kah-PELL-uh, Alioth (Alpha Aurigae): she goat

Caph

kaff (Beta Cassiopei): the branch

Castor

CASS-ter (Alpha Geminorum): ruler, judge

Cheleb

CHAY-leb (Beta Ophiuchi): serpent enfolding

Cursa

CUR-sa (Beta Eridani): bent down

Dabih

DAB-eh (Beta Capricorni): the sacrifice slain

Deneb

DEN-ebb (Alpha Cygni): this from afar, the judge

Deneb al Gedi

DEN-ebb al-JED-eye (Delta Capricorni): the sac-rifice cometh

Denebola

deh-NEB-oh-la (Beta Leonis): the judge who cometh

Diphda

DIP-dah (Beta Ceti): overthrown or thrust down

Dubhe

DUBB-be (Alpha Ursae Majoris): flock

El Nath

el-NATH (Beta Tauri): wounded, slain

Enif

ENN-if (Epsilon Pegasi): nose, the water

Fomalhaut

FOAM-al-ought (Alpha Piscis Austrini): mouth of the fish

Hadar

HAD-ar, Agena ah-JEN-ah (Beta Centauri): knee of the Centaur

Hyades

HY-uh-deez cluster (in Taurus): congregated

Kaus Australis

KOSS os-TRAH-lis (Epsilon Sagittarii): south of the bow

Kaus Borealis

KOSS bor-ee-AL-is (Lambda Sagittarii): north of the bow

Kaus Meridianalis
KOSS oss-TRAY-liss (Delta Sagittarii): middle of the bow

Kochab
KOE-kab (Beta Ursae Minoris): waiting him who cometh

Kornephorus
KOR-ne-for-us (Beta Herculis): kneeling branch

Lesath
LEA-sath (Upsilon Scorpii): perverse

Ma'asym
ma-ASS-em (Lambda Herculis): the sin offering

Markab
MAR-kab (Alpha Pegasi): returning from afar

Marsic
MAR-sik (Chi Herculis): the wounding

Matar
MAH-tar (Eta Pegasi): who causes to overflow; fortunate rain

Mebsuta
meb-SUE-tah (Epsilon Geminorum): treading under foot

Megrez
MEH-grez (Delta Ursae Majoris): tail

Menkalinan
men-KAL-ih-nan (Beta Aurigae): chain of the goats

Menkar
MEN-kar (Alpha Ceti): the chained enemy

Merach, Merak
ME-rack (Beta Ursae Majoris): purchased flock

Mesartim
meh-sar-TIM (Gamma Arietis): the bound

Minchar al Sugia
min-KAR-al-SUG-eh-ah (? Hydrae): the piercing of the deceiver

Mincher al Goreb
MIN-cher al-GOR-eb (Delta Corvi): the raven tearing to pieces

Mira
MY-ruh (Omicron Ceti): the rebel

Mirac, Mizr, Mizar
MY-zar (Epsilon Boötes): the coming forth as an arrow, preserving, guarding

Mirach
MY-rack (Beta Andromedae): the weak

Mirfak
MURR-fak (Alpha Persei): who helps

Mizar
MY-zar (Zeta Ursae Majoris): separate or small

Muphride, Muphrid, Mufrid
MU-frid (Eta Boötes): who separates

Murzim, Mirzam
MURR-zam (Beta Canis Majoris): prince or ruler

Na'ir al Saiph
nay-er-al-SAFE (Iota Orionis): brightly bruised

Nain
nayn (? Sagittarii): gracious one

Nehushta
NEH-ush-tah (? Sagittarii): the going or sending forth

Nekkar
NECK-ker (Beta Boötes): pierced

Nihal
neh-HAL (Beta Leporis): the mad

Okda
AWK-dah (Phi Piscium): united

Phaeda, Phacda
FECK-dah (Gamma Ursae Majoris): visited, guarded, numbered

Pleiades
PLEE-uh-deez cluster (in Taurus): gathering, the congregation of the judge or ruler, seven sisters

Polaris
pole-AIR-iss, Al Ruccaba (Alpha Ursae Minoris): turned or ridden on

Pollux
POLL-lux (Beta Geminorum): who cometh to suffer

Praesepe
PRAY-seh-pea "beehive" cluster (M44 in Cancer), Ma'alaph: a multitude, offspring

Procyon
PRO-see-on (Alpha Canis Minoris): redeemer, rising before the dog

Propus
PRO-pus (Eta Geminorum): the branch

Rakis
RAH-kis (? Leporis): bound with a chain

Ras al Gethi
rahs-al-GETH-ee (Alpha Herculis): head of him who bruises

Ras al Hagus
RAS-el-haig-uss (Alpha Ophiuchi): the head of him who holds

Regulus
REG-you-luss (Alpha Leonis): treading under foot, little king

Rigel
RYE-jell (Beta Orionis): the foot that crushes

Rigil Kentaurus
RYE-jill ken-TOR-us, Toliman TOLL-eh-man (Alpha Centauri): leg of the Centaur, the heretofore and hereafter

Rucbah

RUK-bah, Rukbat (Alpha Sagittarii): the enthroned, the seated, riding of the bowman

Ruchbah

RUK-bah (Delta Cassiopei): the enthroned, the seated

Saad al Melik

sa-ad-al-ME-lick (Alpha Aquarii): the record of the pouring forth

Saad al Suud

sa-ad-al-SU-ud (Beta Aquarii): the pourer out

Sadr

SAD-der (Gamma Cygni): who returns as in a circle

Saiph

safe (Kappa Orionis): bruised

Scheat

SHEE-at (Beta Pegasi): who goeth and returneth

Scheat

SHEE-at, Skat (Delta Aquarii): who goeth and returneth

Schedir

SHED-durr (Alpha Cassiopei): the freed

Sephina

sef-HEE-nah (? Carinae): multitude

Sheliak

SHE-leh-ak (Beta Lyrae): eagle

Sirius

SEER-ee-us (Alpha Canis Majoris): prince, leader of heaven, chief of the host, sparkling one, scorching, dog star

Soheil

so-HEIL (? Carinae): the desired

Spica

SPY-kay, Al Zimach, Tsemech (Alpha Virginis): the branch, ear of corn

Sugia

SUE-gee-ah (? Leporis): the deceiver

Sulaphat

su-LAH-fat (Gamma Lyrae): springing up, ascending

Tarazed

TAR-uh-zed (Gamma Aquilae): wounded, torn

Tegmine

TEG-mine (Zeta Cancri): holding

Thuban

THEW-ban (Alpha Draconis): the subtle

Triphas

TREYE-fas (? Ophiuchi): treading under foot

Tureis

TUR-ace (Iota Carinae): possession in hand

Unuk

YOU-nuk (Alpha Serpentis): encompassing

Vega

VEE-guh (Alpha Lyrae): exaltation, triumph, victory

Wasat

WAY-sat (Delta Geminorum): set

Wesen

WESS-en (Delta Canis Majoris): the bright, the shining

Zaurak

ZAW-rack, Zurak (Gamma Eridani): flowing Zavijaveh (Beta Virginis): the gloriously beautiful

Zozma

ZOZ-mah (Delta Leonis): shining forth

Zuben Akrabi

zoo-ben-ack-RAH-bee (Gamma Librae): the price of the conflict

Zuben al Genubi

zoo-ben-ell-jen-NEW-bee (Alpha Librae): the price deficient

Zuben al Shemali

zoo-ben-ess-sha-MAY-lee (Beta Librae): the price that covers

Star Trails

Glossary of Astronomical and Related Terms

Absolute magnitude

Ab means "away from"; and *solute* (der. *solvere*) means "to loose"; the brightness that a celestial object would appear to have if viewed from a distance of ten parsecs.

Altazimuth mounting

Alt is short for "altitude" and *azimuth* (der. *assumut*) means "the ways" (i.e., directions); a telescope mounting that swings from side to side parallel to the horizon (in azimuth), and up and down (in altitude).

Altitude

Alti means "high"; a rectangular coordinate measure of the vertical; the angular distance of a celestial object above the horizon at sea level.

Angstrom (Å) [angstrom unit (A.U. or a.u.)]

A unit of measure of the wavelength of light (equals 10^{-10} of a meter). It is named after Anders J. Ångström (1814–1874), a Swedish physicist whose pioneer studies in spectroscopy enabled him to discover hydrogen in the Sun in 1862. He mapped the Sun's spectrum in 1868.

Aperture

Apertus means "to open"; the "hole" through which light enters a telescope or camera.

Aphelion

Ap means "away from" and *helios* refers to the "Sun"; for an object orbiting the Sun, the point of the orbit farthest from the Sun.

Apogee

Apo means "away from" and *gee* means "Earth"; for an object orbiting Earth, the point on the orbit farthest from Earth.

Apparent magnitude

Apparent means "appear"; the brightness of a celestial object as seen from Earth.

Arc second

Arc (der. *arcus*) means "bow, arch, curve"; *second* refers to a division of a minute of angular measure ($^1/_{10}$ of 1°; 1° = $^1/_{360}$ of a circle); a unit used to measure angular distance across the sky; it is $^1/_{3600}$ of a degree.

Asterim

Aster means "star"; a pattern of stars identifiable within a constellation, but not itself a constellation. E.g., the "sickle" in Leo.

Astrolabe

Aster means "star" and *labe* (der. *lambane*) means "to take"; an ancient astronomical instrument used for observing the altitude of the stars.

Astrology

Aster means "star" and *logos* means "word, study"— the "word or study of the stars"; a belief system in which the configuration of the sun, moon, planets, and stars are believed to influence human affairs.

Astronomical unit (AU)

The average distance between Earth and the Sun—about 93 million miles.

Astronomy

Aster means the "star" and *nomos* refers to the law; a branch of science that deals with the laws governing celestial bodies.

Axis

Axis means "hub"; an imaginary line through the center of a celestial object around which it rotates.

Azimuth

Azimuth means "the ways" (i.e., directions); a rectangular coordinate measure of the horizontal. It is measured from north, toward east. East = 90°, south = 180°, and west = 270°.

Big Bang theory

The cosmogonic belief system that posits that the universe began as an explosion of a tiny, super hot bundle of matter many billions of years ago.

Binary star

Bi means "two"; two stars linked by a gravitational attraction and revolving around a common center of mass (e.g., Alpha Crucis).

Black hole

A celestial object so dense that no light can escape from it.

Catadioptric telescope

Cata means "down" or "against," *di* means "two", *optric* means "to see" or "make visible"; a telescope (e.g., Schmidt-Cassegrain) that uses both mirrors and lenses to form an image.

Celestial

Celest means "heaven, sky" and *-ial* is a suffix that means "pertaining to"; pertaining to the sky or heavens.

Celestial Equator

An imaginary line encircling the sky midway between the North and South Celestial Poles; the projection of Earth's equator on the Celestial Sphere.

Celestial Poles

Pole means "axis"; the point of intersection of Earth's polar axis with the Celestial Sphere; the projection of Earth's polar axis on the Celestial Sphere.

Celestial Sphere

Sphere means "ball"; an imaginary sphere surrounding Earth upon which all celestial objects seem to hang and can be plotted using right ascension and declination coordinates.

Cepheids

Derived from Cepheus; supergiant stars that pulsate due to change in surface temperature over a period ranging from a few days to a few months.

Circumpolar stars

Circum means "around" and *pole* means "axis"; around the axis; refers to stars that never set and therefore are always seen from a given location on Earth.

Cluster

Any grouping of stars or galaxies.

Conic section

Conic means "cone"; the curve of intersection between a right circular cone and a plane; this curve can be a circle, ellipse, parabola, or hyperbola.

Conjunction

Con means "with, together with" and *junct* means "to join"; to join together; the moment when two celestial objects appear to be very close to each other in the sky.

Constellation

Con means "with, together with" and *stell(a)* is Latin for "star"; stars together; a group of stars that form a picture in the night sky.

Cosmogony

Cosmos means "world, universe" and *gonos* means "origin"; the origin of the universe; the study of ideas about the origin and generation of the universe. These ideas cannot be derived by applying the scientific method. Hence, they must be based upon the underlying convictions or presuppositions (faith positions) of the individual scientist.

Cosmology

Cosmos means "world, universe" and *logos* means "word, study"; the word or study of the universe; the study of the nature and workings of the observable universe.

Culmination

Culmin means "peak, ridge"; occurs when a celestial body reaches its the highest point above an observer's horizon.

Dark adaptation

Ad means "toward" and *apat* (der. *aptare*) means "to fit"; to fit to; what happens when the human eye, under little or no illumination, becomes increasingly sensitive to light from distance objects.

Day

The rotation period of any planet. For Earth, it is the time taken for it to spin on its axis once. The rotation of Earth can be measured relative to the stars (sidereal day) or the Sun (solar day). The mean solar day (the measure of Earth's rotation relative to an imaginary mean Sun, moving across the sky at a uniform rate) is 24 hours in length. The sidereal day lasts 23 hours, 56 minutes, 4 seconds. The mean solar day is 24 hours, 3 minutes, 56.55 seconds of sidereal time.

Decans

Decans means "part"; the thirty-six constellations that have been associated to the twelve constellations of the zodiac from antiquity.

Declination [Dec. or the Greek letter delta, δ]

De means "away from" and *cline* (der. *clinare*) means "to bend"; to bend away from; the angular distance of a celestial object north or south of the Celestial Equator. North of the Celestial Equator, this angular distance is measured from 0° to +90°. South of the Celestial Equator, this angular distance is measured from 0° to -90°. It is equivalent to terrestrial latitude.

Deep Sky or Messier Objects

Objects usually dimmer than stars and requiring a telescope to see (e.g., open clusters, globular clusters, nebulae, galaxies). They include a list of 110 objects compiled by Charles Messier (1730–1817), a French astronomer, to distinguish them from comets. Those objects not making this list are often referred to by their number in the *New General Catalogue* (NGC), compiled by John L. E. Dreyer (1852–1926).

Density

Dens (der. *densus*) means "thick"; the amount of mass contained in a unit volume of an object.

Diurnal

Diurnal (der. *diurnus*) means "daily, of a day"; occurring on a daily basis.

Diurnal circle

The apparent path of a star on the Celestial Sphere due to Earth's daily rotation.

Doppler effect

Named in honor of Christian Doppler (1803–1853), Austrian physicist who studied the nature of sound waves; a phenomenon in which the spectrum of an object rapidly receding from the point of measurement is shifted toward the red wavelength in proportion to the velocity of recession and shifted to the blue similarly, if the object to moving toward the point of measurement.

Dwarf star

Dwarf means "small"; a star that is in the process of contraction while its density is gradually growing greater and greater.

Eclipse

Eclipse means "cessation, abandonment"; occurs when one celestial body passes in from of another, dimming or obscuring its light.

Ecliptic

Ecliptic is derived from the root word *eclipse*; the apparent annual path of the Sun among the stars. It is also the circle of intersection between Earth's orbital plane (tilted at 23.5°) and the Celestial Sphere.

Electromagnetic radiation

Electro means "amber," *magnetic* comes from *Mágnes* (*líthos* or "stone")—the stone of Magnesia or the magnesian stone, and *radiant* (der. *radius*) means "to emit beams or rays"; radiant energy produced by oscillating electric or magnetic charges or fields.

Electromagnetic spectrum

Spectrum (der. *specere*) means "to look at"; the sum total of all known wavelengths of electromagnetic radiation including gamma rays, X rays, ultraviolet rays, visible light, infrared, and radio waves.

Electron

Electro means "amber" and *-on* (der. *ion*) means "to go"; to go amber; a subatomic particle with a negative electric charge that occupies the outer regions of an atom.

Ellipse

Ellipse (der. *ellipsis*) means "to fall short of"; an oval, closed path followed by a celestial object moving under the gravitation attraction of another celestial object (e.g., the path of Earth around the Sun).

Energy

En means "within, in" and *ergon* means "to work"; at work; the ability to do work.

Equator

Equate means "equal"; the great circle on Earth's surface formed by the intersection of a plane passing through Earth's center perpendicular to its axis of rotation.

Equatorial mounting

A telescope mounting that has one axis parallel to Earth's rotational axis. This mounting is very convenient because you can follow the motion of the celestial bodies in the sky with a single movement.

Equinox

Equi means "equal" and *nox* (der. *noct*) means "night"; equal night; occurs when the path of the Sun crosses the Celestial Equator; the beginning of spring (vernal) and autumn (autumnal).

Fission

Fissus means "to split"; the breaking up or "smashing" of heavier nuclei into lighter ones with an attendant release of energy.

Focal length

The distance between a lens or mirror and its focus.

Focal ratio

The ratio of the size of the aperture of a lens or mirror to its focal length.

Focus

The point in an optical system where the image is formed.

Fusion

Fusus means "to melt"; the nuclear "melting" of lighter elements into heavier ones with an attendant conversion of mass into energy.

Galactic anti-center

The point in the sky that is exactly opposite to the hub of the Milky Way galaxy.

Galactic equator

The circle of intersection of the plane of the Milky Way disk with the Celestial Sphere.

Galactic poles

The two points on the celestial sphere 90° from the galactic equator.

Galactic red shift

A calculated shift to the red side of the electromagnetic spectrum that is proportional to the distance that a remote galaxy is from us.

Galactic rotation

The rotational motion of the Milky Way galaxy about its center.

Galaxy

Gala means "milk"; a gigantic gathering of stars, gas, and dust, all bound together by gravity. There are three types of galaxies: spiral, elliptical, and irregular.

Geocentric

Geo means "Earth" and *centric* means "at the center"; having Earth at the center.

Globular star cluster

A spherical cluster that may contain millions of stars (e.g., M13 in Hercules).

Gravitation

Gravitas means "heavy"; the force of attraction of one object on another object.

Gravitational time dilation

Dilat (der. *dilatare*) means "to enlarge, extend"; the force that causes clocks and all physical processes to tick at different rates in different parts of the universe.

Great Circle

Circle (der. *circulus*) means "ring"; any circle on the surface of a sphere whose center coincides with that of the sphere.

Greenhouse effect

The trapping of a planet's radiant energy by its atmosphere.

Handspan

Span means "distance"; when holding the fingers and thumb apart at the end of your outstretched arm, the degree measure from your thumb to your little finger will approximately measure 20°.

Heliacal rising

The rising of a celestial object just before the Sun's rising.

Heliocentric

Helio means "Sun"; having the Sun at the center.

Hertzsprung-Russell (HR) Diagram

Developed by Ejnar Hertzsprung (1873–1967), a Danish astronomer, and Henry N. Russell (1877–1957), an American astronomer; a graph where the horizontal axis plots star temperature (or color) and the vertical axis plots the star's corresponding absolute magnitude.

Horizon

Horiz (der. *horos*) means "limit"; a great circle on the celestial sphere 90° from the observer's zenith.

Light-year

The distance that light travels in one year, about six trillion miles (9.5 trillion kilometers) or 63,240 astronomical units.

Light

That part of the electromagnetic spectrum that can be seen with the human eye.

Lucid star

Lucid (der. *lucere*) means "to shine"; stars that can be seen with the naked eye.

Luminosity

Lumin (der. *lumen*) means "light"; signifies how bright a star is in comparison with the Sun.

Magnification

The apparent size of an object seen through an optical system (e.g., binoculars) compared to its size when viewed with the unaided eye.

Magnitude

Magni means "large"; a logarithmic unit used to measure the optical brightness of celestial objects. The lower the magnitude, the brighter the object. Because it is based on logarithms, a five-fold difference in magnitude represents a 100-fold difference in brightness.

Meridian

Meridi means "midday" and -*an* means "of, pertaining to"; pertaining to midday; an imaginary line on the sky the runs due north and south and passes through the observer's zenith.

Meteor

Met (de. *meta*) means "beyond" and -*eor* (der. *aéirein*) means "to lift, raise"; to lift beyond; a bright trail or streak that appears in the sky when a meteoroid is heated to incandescence by friction with Earth's atmosphere.

Milky Way

A soft, glowing, and somewhat milky band of light encircling the night sky. It is the disk of the spiral galaxy in which the Sun lies as seen from the inside.

Month

A unit of time based upon the Moon's motion around Earth. There are several kinds of months:

(1) **Synodic**—the time it takes for the Moon to go through a complete cycle of phases (lunation), 29 days, 12 hours, 44 minutes, and 2.9 seconds (29.530588 days),

(2) **Sidereal**—the time it takes for the Moon to return to the same position against the star background, 27 days, 7 hours, 43 minutes, and 11.5 seconds (27.321661 days),

(3) **Draconic**—the time between two passages of the Moon through the ascending node (from south to north across the plane of Earth's orbit), 27 days, 5 hours, 5 minutes, and 35.8 seconds (27.21222 days),

(4) **Tropical**—measures the passage of the Moon across the longitude of the equinox and back again, 27 days, 7 hours, 43 minutes, and 4.7 seconds (27.321582 days),

(5) **Anomalistic**—the time between successive perigees in the Moon's orbit, 27 days, 13

hours, 18 minutes, and 33.2 seconds (27.554551 days), and

(6) **Solar**—an artificial unit devised to fit into our calendar; it lasts one-twelfth of a solar year (30.43685 days).

Nadir

Nadir (der. *nazir*) means "opposite"; the point opposite the zenith on the celestial sphere.

Nebula

Nebula means "cloud"; a cloud of gas or dust in space. It may be luminous or dark. An example of a dark nebula is the Coalsack that lies in the Milky Way near the Southern Cross. The Northern Coalsack in Cygnus is almost as notable as its southern counterpart. An example of a luminous nebula is the Horsehead Nebula in Orion.

Neutron star

A gigantic star that has collapsed and now consists almost wholly of neutrons.

Neutron

Neutron is derived from *neutr*, "to go neutral"; a subatomic particle that has about the same mass as a proton but has no electric charge.

Nova

Nova means "new"; a star that brightens suddenly by several magnitudes as it partially explodes in a thermonuclear reaction.

Nucleus

Nuc (der. *nux*) means "nut" and *-leus* is a diminutive suffix; inner part of a nut, kernel; the central region of an atom or a galaxy.

Objective

Objective (der. *objectare*) means "to throw before"; the main light-gathering lens or mirror of a telescope.

Occultation

Occult means "to conceal"; the covering up of one celestial object by another.

Ocular

Ocul (der. *oculus*) means "eye" and *-ar* is a suffix meaning "pertaining to"; eyepiece.

Open (galactic) star cluster

A group of a few hundred stars bound together by gravity and traveling through space together. The Hyades and the Pleiades are examples of open clusters.

Orbit

Orbit (der. *orbitus*) means "circular"; the path followed by any celestial object moving under the control of another celestial object's gravity.

Parallax

Para means "at or to one side of, among" and *allax* (der. *allássein*) means "to exchange"; to exchange beside or among; a method whereby astronomers can measure stellar distances by measuring the apparent change in position of a nearby star due to Earth's orbital motion around the Sun.

Parsec

Combined from **par**allax and **sec**ond; a unit of distance equal to 3.26 light years or 206,265 astronomical units. It is the distance at which a star would have a parallax of 1 arc second.

Perigee

Peri- means "near, around" and *gee* means "Earth"; near or around Earth; the point of closest approach to Earth of an object in Earth orbit.

Perihelion

Peri means "near, around" and *helio* means "Sun"; near or around Sun; the point of closest approach to the Sun of an object orbiting the Sun.

Period

Peri means "around" and *od* (der. *hodos*) means "way, circuit"; around way, circuit; the interval of time required for an event to repeat itself.

Planetarium

Planet means "wandering" and *arium* means "used for, for the purpose of"; used for wandering; an optical instrument that can project representations of the night sky and its associated phenomena onto a domed ceiling.

Planetary nebula

Planet means "wandering" and *nebula* means "cloud"; wandering cloud; a bright, spherical nebula that surrounds a hot central star. It appears as a planetary disk in a telescope (e.g., the Owl Nebula [M97] in Ursa Major).

Polaris

A guiding star in celestial navigation because of its relative constancy (due to its current close proximity to the North Pole).

Precession

Pre means "before" and *cess* means "to go, yield"; to go before; a slow, periodic wobble in Earth's axis caused by the combined gravitational pull of the Sun and the Moon.

Prism

Prism (der. *prisma*) means "something sawed"; a triangular piece of glass that can break up light into its component colors and create a spectrum.

Proton

Proton (der. *protos*) means "to go first"; a subatomic particle that carries a positive electric charge and is, along with the neutron, a basic component of atomic nuclei.

Pulsar

Pulsar (der. *pulsus*) means "to beat"; a spinning neutron star that emits periodic bursts of radio energy.

Quasar [*quas(i-stell)ar*]

Quasi means "resembling, like" and *stellar* means "star"; starlike; a celestial object or radio source that, in its spectrum, displays a marked redshift; a void.

Radio star

Radio (der. *radiation*) refers to "radiant light or energy"; stars that give no visible light but can be detected by radio telescopes.

Reflector telescope

Re means "back" and *flect* means "to flex, bend"; to flex back; a telescope that forms an image with mirrors.

Refractor telescope

Re means "back" and *fract* means "to break, force"; to break back; a telescope that forms an image with lenses.

Relativity

Re means "back" and *lat* (der. *latus*) means "to carry"; to carry back; a description of motion that deals with the behavior of objects moving at very high velocities or in very strong gravitational fields.

Resolution

Re means "back" and *solu* (der. *solvere*) means "untie, release"; to untie or release back; the degree to which fine details are delineated in an image.

Resolving power

The ability of an optical instrument to observe fine detail.

Retrograde motion

Retro means "behind" and *grade* (der. *gradus*) means "to step, go"; a step behind; the apparent westward motion of a planet relative to the stars.

Revolution

Re means "back" and *volu* (der. *volvere*) means "to roll, turn around"; to roll back; the orbital motion of one celestial object about another.

Right ascension [R.A. or the Greek letter alpha, α]

A- (der. *ad*) means "toward, up" and *scens* (der. *scendere*) means "to climb"; to climb toward; the celestial coordinate similar to terrestrial longitude. It measures from zero hours to twenty-three hours (where 1 hour = 15°).

Rotation

Rota (der. *rotare*) means "revolve"; the spinning motion of an object about an axis passing through itself.

Scientific notation

Scient means "to know," *fic* (der. *ficus*) means "of, pertaining to," and *nota* means "sign, mark"; a sign or mark of knowledge; a short hand notation for writing large numbers (e.g., 3,000,000,000 in scientific notation is 3×10^9).

Sidereal period

Sidere refers to "star, constellation" and *-al* is a suffix that means "of, pertaining to"; pertaining to a star or constellation; the time (relative to the stars) needed for a planet or moon to make one rotation around its primary body.

Sidereal time

A method of measuring time based on the rotation of Earth relative to the stars, rather than to the Sun (solar time). The sidereal day is about four minutes shorter than the solar day and begins when the vernal equinox crosses the observer's meridian.

Solstice

Sol refers to the "Sun" and *stice* means "to make stand"; to make the Sun stand; occurs when the Sun is at its greatest declination from the Celestial Equator; the shortest day of winter and the longest day of summer.

Spectrograph

Spectro means "to look at" and *graph* means "writing"; writing to look at; an instrument that breaks the light from a celestial object into its component colors.

Spectroscopic parallax

The parallax (or distance) obtained for a star by comparing its apparent magnitude with it absolute magnitude as deduced from the star's spectral characteristics.

Spectrum

Spectrum means "to look at"; the radiant energy from an object spread out into its component wavelengths by some dispersive device like a prism or grating.

Star

A gigantic atomic furnace where heat is generated by the conversion of hydrogen into helium.

Supernova

A cataclysmic explosion of a gigantic star. As it totally disintegrates, it throws off gaseous debris fields.

Telescope

Tele means "end, complete" and *scope* means "to view carefully"; to view carefully the end (afar off); an optical device that enhances the astronomer's view of the heavens.

Temperature

Temper means "adjust, moderate, temper"; tempering or moderating; the measure of the internal energy of a body.

Terrestrial

Terr means "earth" and *-ial* means "pertaining to"; pertaining to Earth.

Triangulation

Tri means "three" and *angul* means "corners"; three corners; a method of determining the distance to an inaccessible point by computing elements of a triangle involving that point.

Tropic of Cancer

Tropic means "to turn"; the parallel of latitude on Earth over which the Sun stands at the winter solstice (in the Southern Hemisphere) and summer solstice (in the Northern Hemisphere); 23.5° N latitude. About 2,000 years ago, the Sun lay in the constellation of Cancer at the Northern Hemisphere's summer solstice. Because of precession, the summer solstice has moved into Gemini and, by the end of the century, it will have moved into Taurus.

Tropic of Capricorn

The parallel of latitude on Earth over which the Sun stands at the winter solstice (in the Northern Hemisphere) and the summer solstice (in the Southern Hemisphere); 23.5° S latitude. Like the Tropic of Cancer, the Northern Hemisphere's winter solstice used to lie in the constellation Capricorn. It now lies in the constellation Sagittarius.

Uniformitarianism

Uni means "one" and *form* (der. *formus*) means "form"; one form; the belief that the actions of existing physical processes (whether it be astronomic, biologic, or geologic) are sufficient to account for all past changes and for the present state of the state of things. The principle of uniformity in present processes is a valid scientific and Scriptural concept (see Genesis 8:22). Uniformitarianism comes into conflict with biblical revelation when it is used to deny the possibility of past (e.g., the Genesis Flood) or future suspension or alteration of these processes by the will and purpose of God.

Variable star

Vary means "alter"; a designation for a star that varies in brightness, with periods ranging from minutes to years. E.g., Betelgeuse in Orion.

Year

Year means "course, circle, to run"; the time required for Earth to complete one orbit of the Sun. There are several kinds of years:

(1) **Tropical**—based upon our calendar (365.2422 days),

(2) **Sidereal**—orbit of Earth with respect to the star background (365.2564 days), and

(3) **Anomalistic**—the interval between two successive perihelion passages of Earth (365.2596 days).

Zenith

Zenith (der. *samt*) means "road over head"; the point on the Celestial Sphere directly overhead of the observer.

Zodiac

Zodiac (der. *zoad*) means "path, way, step"; the twelve constellations that straddle the Ecliptic through which the Sun, Moon, and planets appear to move throughout the year and known from antiquity.

Halley's Comet

Scripture Index

General Index

Ring Nebula

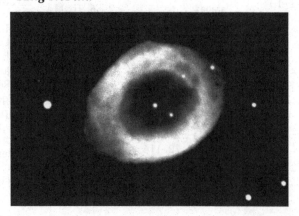

Notes

Notes

Notes

Notes

Notes

Notes

Notes

Notes

Notes

Notes

Notes

Notes